PRAISE FO

MW00583535

"If you teach science, you need this book! *The Science Box* is overflowing with meaningful, engaging lessons that will turn any science classroom into a place of wonder. The ideas are magical yet practical, and Kim and Adam do a beautiful job of showing teachers with limited time and budgets how to bring science to life. They have filled the pages with countless ways for busy teachers to organize and implement lessons that will effectively teach the curriculum while simultaneously creating a love for learning in every student. We are fortunate to learn from their wisdom and experience!"

—**Kim Bearden,** cofounder and executive director
of the Ron Clark Academy

"I can't say enough good things about *The Science Box*. This must-read book is a brilliant invitation to help incorporate meaningful and engaging science experiments into the classroom. Adam Peterson and Kim Adsit are experts in fostering a love of science in the classroom while reaching all students! A big help to all early education educators!"

—**Brittany Bacharach,** owner of Stay at Home Activity Mom

"Finally, a book that not only helps get students excited about science but actually gets EDUCATORS excited and ready to *teach* science. *The Science Box* is more than a book—it's an easy-to-follow tool kit and source of inspiration for any teacher who wants to make it easier for their elementary students to be inspired and curious about the world around them. Packed with perfectly sequenced experiments, lessons, and hacks to make teaching science easier and more hands-on, *The Science Box* earns its place on every elementary school teacher's bookshelf. So obviously written by two people who've been in the trenches—this is the book I wish MY teachers had when I was a kid!"

—**Jerry Kolber,** creator of the *Who Smarted?* podcast, *Brain Games* on the National Geographic channel, and *Brainchild* on Netflix

"Adsit and Peterson paint a realistic, relevant, and implementable approach to science that is accessible to educators of all levels of experience and ages of learners. Their combined experience along with storytelling and insight from guest scientists creates a unique collection of inspiration, accessible resources, and support to implement engaging scientific investigations in learning spaces of all kinds. This book is perfect for pre-service educators, new classroom teachers, seasoned classroom teachers, museum educators, park interpreters, homeschool families, learning commons facilitators, afterschool program leaders, summer camp educators—basically, if you are involved in education, specifically science education, you want this book!"

—**Becky Schnekser,** elementary educator, field scientist, and author of *Expedition Science: Empowering Learners Through Exploration*

"What an incredible resource filled with ideas to make science come alive in your elementary classroom! Your little learners will be thinking like scientists as they are taken through the scientific method by engaging in discussions, hands-on activities, room transformations, and more! Adam and Kim outline a daily plan and break down what to include in your science boxes so that all materials are prepped and ready to go for each standard. This will be my go-to science resource from now on!"

—**Sharyn Kish,** 2020 Ohio Teacher of the Year, District 5, kindergarten teacher, content creator, and presenter

"Adam and Kim are bringing science to life with their fun-filled collection of activities for the primary classroom. This is a must-have for all teachers who wish to provide a hands-on and engaging experience for every student in their classroom!"

—**Jessica Travis,** early childhood specialist and national presenter

"Kim and Adam always know how to add their special sauce to everything they do. They can turn the mundane into the best lesson ever! This book is filled with magic moments just waiting to happen in your own classroom! Not only are they highly engaging and well thought out, but these ideas are also grounded in best practices! It's a win-win! You will win because you won't run short of ideas. Your students will win because you brought these lessons to LIFE!"

—**Deedee Wills,** curriculum specialist and educational author behind Mrs. Wills Kindergarten

"This book helps teachers reflect on how and why they teach science and STEM to little learners. The ideas and strategies shared here are engaging and easy to implement for teachers. It shows how to build activities around various science standards to enhance student learning and their love of science using materials already in the classroom or school environment. This book will get teachers excited to teach science again!"

—**Jackie Kops,** CEO and teacher of Pocket of Preschool

THE SCIENCE BOX

THE SCIENCE BOX

EXPERIMENTS AND EXPLORATIONS THAT DRIVE STUDENT ENGAGEMENT

KIM ADSIT AND **ADAM PETERSON**

This book is available at special discounts when purchased in quantity for educational purposes or for use as premiums, promotions, or fundraisers. For inquiries and details, contact the publisher at books@daveburgessconsulting.com.

Published by Dave Burgess Consulting, Inc.
San Diego, CA
DaveBurgessConsulting.com

Library of Congress Control Number: 2023931717
Paperback ISBN: 978-1-956306-45-3
Ebook ISBN: 978-1-956306-46-0

Illustrations copyright Melonheadz Illustrating
Cover and interior design by Liz Schreiter
Edited and produced by Reading List Editorial
ReadingListEditorial.com

CONTENTS

FOREWORD

In a lonely corner of room 102, a wiry brunette girl sat curled up in her chair staring out the fogged-up window. As her teacher wrote meaningless numbers and words across the chalkboard, the girl's mind went somewhere different. She was swallowed up by thoughts of what else she could be doing. She was affectionately known to peers and adults alike as the girl with dirt under her fingernails and holes in her jeans. If you needed to find her, all you had to do was check the creek. She would inevitably be up to her knees in water, flipping over rocks and looking for creatures. She'd spend hours upon hours fishing, caterpillar hunting, and collecting leaves. She and her dad would go on long walks through the woods, where he would teach her everything there was to know about the outdoors.

The girl's teacher gruffly called her name, and she snapped back to the present. She reminded herself that she hated school. As she resumed staring out the classroom window, she wondered what the critters were doing. It had to be better than adding numbers together. If only her teacher could bring what she loved into the classroom, maybe it would motivate her? With some cardboard boxes, paper towel rolls, and tape, she could have added up those numbers creatively, doing what the teacher wanted her to do.

This little girl was me, Katie Blue—now a published children's book author, national speaker, and veteran teacher with a master's degree. For years, I daydreamed in class as teachers taught topics I didn't care about out of textbooks and gave me homework that I never did. Should I have cared more? Perhaps. But as educators, it is our responsibility to find ways to connect to our students. And what better way is there than to bring our students' interests and passions into our instruction?

As a longtime kindergarten teacher, I have met many other "Katies"—kids who are driven by nature, curiosity, and discovery. It has been and remains my teaching mission to bring those elements into my classroom. Whether it's creating engaging science labs, integrating science into math and literacy, or simply heading outside with my students to explore, the love of science runs through my veins and hopefully translates to my classroom.

Fostering a love of science breeds innovation and creativity, and isn't that what we desire in all our students? So why do we not see science more often in the elementary setting? I've been asking that question for years, and answers have ranged from "available time" to "a focus on testing in literacy and math" to "it's messy." While there may be elements of truth in those sentiments, Kim and Adam can put every teacher's mind at ease. The explorations you'll find throughout this book offer exciting learning opportunities paired with simple setup to help you address the science standards in fun and engaging ways with little prep on your end.

So here is my challenge to you: If you're a teacher who feels like you have the passion to teach science in your classroom, spread that energy! Be a role model and open your classroom so others can see that it's possible. If you're on the fence about the value of teaching science or your ability to effectively teach it, then you're in the right place. Kim and Adam will be your guides.

As for me? I eventually found what my young mind yearned for. And it didn't take much! Ms. H. assigned a leaf-collecting project and I was all in. I found every leaf imaginable and could talk about each one. From then on, Ms. H. had my attention. Of course, not every assignment was science or nature related, but she had found her way to my heart, and that was a direct pathway to my brain. Whether you're a leader in science teaching or just getting the ball rolling, Adam and Kim provide the knowledge to ensure that you're full of ideas you can bring to your classroom tomorrow. Your students will thank you for allowing their minds to wander into a world that celebrates and cultivates scientific inquiry and wonder!

—Katie Blue Mense

PREFACE

Let's start this book with a bit of honesty, shall we? Have you ever said the words "I'm a science teacher"? If you're anything like us, you might not find yourself using that phrase too often. We completely understand if you're a teacher who doesn't consider yourself a science teacher. We've been there. The importance of English language arts and math in today's education system often overpowers all other aspects of the curriculum, leaving little room for subjects like science to shine. This is one of the reasons teaching can be the hardest job you'll ever love. On top of the existing stress weighing us down, many teachers have to create their own science lessons because they don't have access to a curriculum—or the science curriculum they do have access to is nothing but additional reading activities, reading-material work sheets, videos, and the occasional experiment. While each of those resources might be backed by good intentions, they lack two key words we use when discussing science: *experience* and *engagement*.

We strongly believe that for children to fully understand science, they must experience science in an engaging way. In this book we're going to share some of our favorite experiences teaching science at the elementary level. It's important to note that while we've spent our careers in the primary grades, the strategies we've developed to create our engaging lessons and experiments can easily be adapted for scientific studies in all grade levels—you just need a little creativity. We've also cited specific examples throughout the book that will help you make connections between science and other core subjects so you can teach more content in less time.

So, how did the two of us end up writing a book together? What do a retired teacher from Georgia and an Illinois educator in the middle of his career have in common? Let's start by traveling back to the spring of 2006.

ADAM

Kim, an expert kindergarten teacher and nationally known presenter, was speaking to a group of teachers at an event in Illinois. I was a first-year kindergarten teacher attending her presentation. In it, Kim shared how she used an iPod (think the classic click-wheel design) to shuffle music in her classroom. With my mind blown by this genius idea (I was still using cassettes and CDs that had been handed down from my mentor teacher), I approached Kim and asked question after question about this new and exciting way to manage classroom music. The following year, and for several after that, I attended Kim's sessions at the same event. Each year Kim would easily recognize me—when you're the only guy in a group, you stand out. At some point Kim suggested I should throw my hat into the ring to be a presenter. And the rest, as they say, is history. We began doing a few joint sessions at conferences and working on projects together. It was through this that we discovered our shared interest in play, processes, and engagement. We both quickly realized that no matter the conversation we were having, science always seemed to come up as a favorite teaching subject. We also learned that we complement each other very well. Kim brings the organization to my crazy ideas, and I bring the out-of-the-box thinking to her carefully laid-out plans. While our approach can be very different—people often say Kim is type A and I'm type Z—our philosophy is in sync.

So, that's how it all started for us. But how did it start for me?

I don't remember much about my earliest years of elementary school, though I had some of the most fantastic teachers in the world. I can't really remember the lessons or how they were taught, but I do remember all those teachers by name over thirty years later, and I'm still in contact with some of them to this day. So, if it wasn't the lessons or content that was memorable, what was it? Experiences. I remember the experiences I had in each of their classes. While most of what I remember involved learning about books and writing, I can also recall math and social studies experiences. Notice I didn't mention science. Hmm . . . a book about science and I'm only talking about other subjects. I'm not saying we didn't do some great science experiments here and there, but I feel like my science classes were a lot like the ones I was teaching when I first started in my kindergarten classroom. Videos, a lot of work pages, and the occasional experiment. These types of lessons leave little room for experiences.

Fast-forward to high school. I fell in love with science because of the experiments I got to experience in real life—not just through a video or work sheet. From chemistry (where we created concoctions with different elements) to biology (where we got to dissect various creatures), science was definitely more engaging to me when taught in this format. How many of you can still remember the smell in the hallways when dissections were underway in biology classes?

I'm a prime example of how engagement and experience can help even the most reluctant of learners. I wasn't a straight-A student, but I wasn't a failing student. I got by with hard work when it mattered, but I didn't really enjoy it. Science, on the other hand, gave me a place where hard work was also extremely enjoyable.

KIM

Elementary school was a long time ago for me—and coming from an air force family, I moved a lot when I was young. So when Adam first asked me about my elementary school science experiences, I thought, "Are you for real? I can't remember my high school days, much less what happened in the first grade!"

But two of my most vivid memories are from high school. I can still remember my southern literature teacher bringing texts alive

through drama and engagement. She would dance around the room and use character voices as she read aloud to us. That's right, in a high school—reading aloud to children! She didn't just want to teach the standards required; she wanted to instill a love of literature in us. No matter what book she assigned to us, I couldn't wait to get home and read the next chapter.

I also remember the class where I learned about Shakespeare. We created costumes and props to enhance the experience as we acted out the plays we were reading. The learning was engaging every day, which meant that I couldn't wait to get to class.

It might seem weird that I'm writing about language arts in a science book. Why wouldn't I be telling you about all the wonderful science experiences I had? The answer is simple: these language arts experiences were the most memorable for me because I was deeply engaged.

I entered college knowing that I wanted to be a teacher. Although I originally thought I wanted to teach high school math, after a rotation at the early learning center I knew I would land in the primary grades. In 1982 I started teaching kindergarten in Forsyth, Georgia, in a small classroom next door to my college roommate's class. It was there that I learned about the power of play. Our curriculum was focused on teaching kids how to create their own learning. My teacher mentors instilled both ideas and encouragement in me as I found my own way and created my own ideas—just like our students. Science was a regular part of our day. We created environments that encouraged children to explore, question, and experiment.

After sixteen years at that school, I moved back to my hometown. Talk about mixed emotions! I was leaving a team of amazing teachers I was comfortable with and a place where kids were happy and learning. But having the chance to move back home turned out to be just what I needed, both personally and professionally. It was during my teaching career in Houston County that I learned to put a solid framework to my students' learning. I learned about the workshop model of teaching and about what it looks like when the scientific process is applied to the wonderful play experiences I had learned to use in Forsyth. I never looked back. Regardless of the subject we are teaching, we can use experiences to create memories and make learning engaging and enjoyable.

WHAT CAN I DO?

This is the key we encourage you to remember as you plan lessons for the different types of learners in your classroom: Think of ways to make learning enjoyable and engaging while also tackling the hard work that some of your students will thrive on. Ask yourself the following questions: What can I do *today* to engage all my learners in at least one way? What can I do *every single day* to make sure my lessons engage all my learners in as many ways as possible?

Take a minute and make a list of ways you can answer those questions. Our guess is that because you're an amazing educator, you will imagine a variety of ways to take your learning to the next level of engagement. Now, take that list and make sure that each student's learning style is being met in at least one way. If so, you'll be reaching all students through engagement and experiences in ways they may not have had the opportunity to experience before.

We are fascinated by the minds of young children and the different ways in which they learn, and we are passionate about working with teachers to give them content that is practical and easy to implement in their own classrooms—with as little preparation and planning as possible. We want to help you create experiences that excite your students and get them begging for more, and we want to challenge you to explore science in your classroom in ways you might have been hesitant to try before.

In this book, we'll start with how we introduce students to science and celebrate this amazing subject together as a class. You will learn how we help create the "real scientist" mindset in each of our students and how we strategically teach them so that they retain the steps of the scientific process. We'll introduce you to our special tool, the Science Box, which we use to entice our learners each and every week during our science lessons. You'll see how we easily create experiments mostly from items we already have in our classrooms. We'll show you how we help our students meet the Next Generation Science Standards (NGSS) through engaging, purposeful experiments, and you'll get to meet some guest scientists (amazing teacher friends of ours) along the way. We'll also share ideas that will help you make connections between science and other subjects, and we'll leave you ready to hit the laboratory running. Before you know it, you'll be creating science experiences for your own students.

Does that sound good? We hope you're as excited as we are to bring the magic and wonder of science to your classroom full of eager young learners. We've witnessed this transformation with our own students and in the countless classrooms we've visited over the years. We're thrilled for you to join us on this journey as we share the ways we engage all learners through science experiences. So, button up your lab coat and put on your safety goggles because we're about to experiment and explore as we experience science together!

SPECIAL SECTIONS IN THE BOOK

You'll see some special sections throughout the book. Here's what you can expect:

WHAT'S IN THE BOX?

Each activity in the book contains a unique "What's in the Box" section. In these sections you'll find an explanation of the concept the activity will explore as well as a list of the materials you'll need. This will help you determine if the activity will meet your standards and objectives without having to read through the entire experiment. We have provided the list to help make material gathering simpler and more efficient.

CROSS-CURRICULAR CONNECTIONS

Cross-curricular connections are a staple of teaching, and thematic units and integrated curricula have always been among our favorite ways to engage students and teach content across many subjects. It's excellent for intertwining science, reading, math, social studies, and more. Another great way to achieve this is through different types of books. We often find ourselves beginning a unit with a selection of texts. The content and standard-driven potential of these selections guide our instruction. Pairing fiction and nonfiction text is a common practice among teachers, and we'll explore why we support this instructional choice.

There are many facets to a child's comprehension of a selected fiction text. Can she read the words? Does he spend too much time decoding words, resulting in a lack of comprehension? But we need to remember that there is much more to comprehension than a child's ability to decode or read the words. If a child lacks the schema for the topic, they may be unable to make predictions, form connections, or comprehend the text. It's no secret that if a child is uninterested in a subject, they will need something more to engage them in text about that subject. We'll share examples from read alouds and thematic units that help engage all learners, increase connections between subjects, and get your students excited to experience learning through science and more.

GUEST SCIENTIST SECTIONS

We have both been super lucky in our teaching careers to meet and become friends with some extraordinary educators from many different places. We've invited some of them along on our writing journey to share their favorite science experiments and explorations. We're honored to share their knowledge and experience with you.

INTRODUCTION:
WHAT IS SCIENCE AND WHAT DOES A SCIENTIST DO?

Before we dive into the exciting experiments and engagement strategies in store for you, let's consider what science is, what it looks like, and what it can become in an elementary classroom. Every teacher is different. Every classroom is different. And guess what? That's OK! This is something we preach to teachers and administrators every time we present. Your classroom should reflect you and your students. How do you ensure that? Get to know your students, build relationships, and—the easiest way—ask. We love using student and parent surveys at the beginning of the year to learn as much about our new learners as possible. Another fun activity is called Kid of the Day. At the beginning of the year, highlight one of your students each day during your morning meeting time. Discuss their name, their favorite things, and whatever else you want. Including this as part of your daily routine helps you learn about your students and helps them learn about each other.

WHAT IS SCIENCE?

If someone asked you to explain what science looks like in your classroom, what words would you use? We're willing to bet one of those words is *experiment*. Like we mentioned in our preface, experiments and hands-on activities are what we remember from our own childhood science classes.

But what about your students? What words do you think they would use to describe science in your classroom? It probably depends on their experiences in and out of school. We posed this question on social media, requesting that parents ask their children what science means to them. These are some of the responses we received:

"Science is when we get to have fun and blow stuff up!"

"Science is mixing minerals together."

"Science is doing experiments to figure out an answer to a question."

"Science is fun and amazing like doing fun experiments and stuff."

"Science is where you make potions and experiment with something."

"Science is stuff you learn. It's making a volcano with powder and vinegar and you make it explode!"

"Science is the world's greatest mystery being solved."

"Science is experimenting, testing out things, seeing how things work and what they do."

Now, reread those statements from the mouths of kids and see what words come up the most. The ones that stand out to us—and that explain why we teach science the way we do—are "experiments," "learn," and "fun." But if you look closely at each of those statements, something else makes a strong case for why children love science: action! Kids love to be involved and love to learn by doing. Doing experiments, blowing stuff up, making potions—all these learning moments are memorable to students because action engages them in the learning process. When you use a teaching strategy that involves your students physically doing something, not only is the learning more engaging, but it also sticks! As teachers we are constantly looking for ways to make sure our students are retaining knowledge of a subject, standard, or skill. The statements above prove that knowledge retention can be accomplished more easily when your students are involved in the learning process and are able to *do* rather than just *sit and get*.

Now, ask yourself the same question again. When you look at your classroom, your lessons, and your teaching style, what is science? Does science in your classroom reflect any of the key words used by the kids who answered our question? Does science in your classroom involve doing, making, mixing, or blowing stuff up? If not, that's OK! Our classrooms didn't always reflect those words, either. It was a journey for each of us to design science strategies and styles that would reach each of our students and help them learn to love science as much as we do. You'll see as you read on that all it takes is a little making, doing, and mixing it all together with fun to create engaging science lessons that your kiddos will love.

WHAT DOES A SCIENTIST DO?

New scientific discoveries are being made every single day, and different variables cause different results. The most important thing we can do for our students is present content in an engaging way that will encourage creative, adaptive thinking to help them better focus on the standards we are trying to present. While there will always be different ways of doing things and various ways to get results in experiments, one thing doesn't change: the process we use to get from observations to end results. This is called the scientific process. At the primary level, most of what we teach in science revolves around getting students to understand this process so they're better prepared for future science lessons in other grade levels.

Before we teach the steps of the scientific process, we dedicate time to accessing our students' prior knowledge through questions like these: What is a scientist? What does a scientist do? Where might a scientist work? This is a perfect opportunity to use technology and the wealth of information available at your fingertips. We love using videos to share information with our students and to introduce them to real-life experiences and people. A simple YouTube search for "scientist videos for kids" will retrieve many options that introduce and explain basic science terms, experiments, and more. A simple, eye-catching anchor chart can inspire participation from even the most reluctant learners. And reaching out to your local zoo, chemical plants, hospitals, and doctor's offices for possible guest speakers can be an effective way to connect your learners with various types of scientists in their own community. When students see a familiar face or someone from their community working in an area of interest, it can make their own dreams seem more reachable. It can help reinforce the idea that they can be anything they want to be—including a scientist. Utilizing these tools and strategies from the start of your science exploration will lay a foundation for your learners to build on each time you begin a new experiment.

THE SCIENTIFIC PROCESS MADE SIMPLE

We're both big believers in visual learning cues that offer all types of learners opportunities to access information in ways that suit them best. As we introduce our science units to students, we include visuals that will help our young scientists recall and use the strategies we will be teaching them. It's safe to assume that some students entering the primary grades may have had exposure to simple science experiments at home or elsewhere. There's an abundance of YouTube videos, Pinterest boards, and blogs that show families how to experiment with bath bombs, slime, and other viral science-esque crazes. But for most of the children in our classrooms, the actual six-step process of thinking like a scientist is new.

Now, you might be thinking, "My preschoolers can't even mix paint colors without making a mess. How am I going to get them to understand the scientific process?" First, don't forget that making a mess with colors is a great way to learn responsibility, cause and effect, and step-by-step instruction. Second, we've broken the steps down to make them easy for even the youngest learner to comprehend and put to use. So have no fear: no matter what grade level you teach, your little learners will be reminding you if you skip a step!

STEP 1: SCIENTISTS MAKE AN OBSERVATION

"Take a look at this piece of fruit, friends!" "Wow, look at these bugs crawling here!" "Look at that gap where a bridge is supposed to be!"

It's no secret that the enthusiasm your children feel for any given subject is a direct reflection of the excitement you show for it first. This is especially true when you're introducing your learners to a brand-new idea or topic. Encouraging students to observe an actual item, rather than just telling them about it or showing an image, can make all the difference in their interest level. Novelty breeds learning, and nothing is more of a novelty to children than being able to physically observe, touch, and manipulate real objects in the classroom. Observation is the first step in many tasks we expect our learners to complete each day. When we teach new letters, we first ask our students to look at a representation of a letter. When we teach number sense, we first ask our children to observe the number in different formats such as numerals, dot combinations, and tally marks.

Observation is an important step in science, just as it is in other subjects. However, the way you present material during a scientific observation step can have a profound impact on how the rest of the lesson goes. Because many science experiences in the primary grades focus on exploring the world around you, displaying and manipulating objects from the world provides both hands-on experience and a sense of connection to the world. This creates the opportunity for deeper understanding and application of that understanding to other content. For example, if you've ever done a lesson on how plants grow, you've most likely shown a video or image of the roots of a plant. That's great; the children have now been exposed to the item they're going to be studying. But what if instead of an image or video, you brought in various types of real plants with their root systems still intact? Just imagine students' excitement when you pull out a giant cornstalk with dirt-covered roots dangling below, or when you lay different types of flowers across the floor to display the delicate roots that are usually hidden below ground. Your students will be fascinated and will want to learn more about an object when they get to see it firsthand. It's even better when an object is foreign to them or something they've had little experience with before in their lives—because that automatically sets the stage for the second step of the scientific process.

FUN OBSERVATION IDEAS TO TRY

- Give each student a magnifying glass and let them explore classroom resources, manipulatives, the carpet, and other spaces around the classroom.
- Take a walk outside and observe the world around your school.
- Give students different types of coins and currency to observe similarities and differences. Look at different cereal pieces under a magnifying glass or microscope.
- On your big screen, share Google search images of items under a microscope.

STEP 2: SCIENTISTS ASK QUESTIONS

"What the heck is that thing?" "Where did you find those shells?" "What happened to that apple?"

Young learners are constantly asking questions about things in their classrooms, schools, and lives. We all have those students who never stop asking questions, right? While constant questioning can sometimes push a teacher to the brink of insanity, there is no better time to encourage questioning than during science lessons. When kids are genuinely interested in a topic, questions will naturally follow. Yet there are always soft-spoken students or students who lack the confidence to speak up during class for fear of being wrong. This is another reason we focus so much time on open questioning during science lessons. Using real-life items for observations and encouraging questions from all students can help build confidence in even your most reluctant learner.

One of our favorite activities to do during the questioning step of the scientific process is called I Write, You Write. It ensures that children are actively engaged in the lesson. As you write questions and observations on a chart, children record that information into an observation notebook. Observation notebooks can be any type of notebook containing blank paper. They can be spiral-bound notebooks or paper that has been stapled together. Don't get too hung up if students aren't getting every word you're writing; it's about the process of recording the questions. The observation notebook can also be a space for them to work at their own pace and draw or write their own questions. This is just one example of how science can level the learning playing field. There is no right or wrong when observing and asking questions.

FUN QUESTION IDEAS TO TRY

- Show images from Photosforclass.com on your big screen and encourage students to ask questions about them.

- Bring in a rotten piece of fruit or moldy bread and see what questions students come up with.

- Allow students to write or draw their questions on sticky notes (great for those who don't want to vocally ask) and stick them to an anchor chart.

STEP 3: MAKE A HYPOTHESIS

"I think . . ." "I hope to see . . ." "I'm excited for . . ."

We've all started classroom discussions with the words "Who can guess . . ." And we've all observed hands shooting up in the air. Students love to make guesses about things they see or hear in hopes of being the first one to get a correct answer. (Well, let's be honest, sometimes their eagerness to speak is simply fueled by their burning desire to share something that happened over the weekend.) In science, when you ask children to make a hypothesis about a given concept, some students may be experiencing the content in question for the first time while others may be more familiar with it. Either way, a variety of questions will surely surface.

Getting children to guess is easy, but getting them to make an *educated* guess can be a bit trickier. This is why we put so much effort into teaching students what *hypothesis* means and modeling what it looks like to come up with one. Remember, kids learn best when they're *doing*, and these first three steps of the scientific process can include a lot of engaging, hands-on activity—long before we get to conducting actual experiments. We encourage educated guesses by relating the content at hand to familiar items or experiences.

But what about the students who have more experience and are blurting out hypotheses or answers before you can stop them? Well, why stop them? If a child experienced a similar experiment in a previous grade level or saw a video of it being done, this offers a perfect opportunity to explain the beauty of science experiments: that results aren't always exactly the same. Add your eager young guesser's hypothesis to the board and see how the experiment turns out this time around.

FUN HYPOTHESIS IDEAS TO TRY

- Allow students to write or draw their hypothesis on sticky notes (great for those reluctant students) and stick them to an anchor chart.

- Invite students to turn and talk with a partner about their hypothesis and explain their reason behind it.

STEP 4: CONDUCT AN EXPERIMENT

"Go get your PPE on!" "We are going to do an experiment with . . ." "Let's see what happens when . . ."

This is the part all your budding scientists have been waiting for! There's nothing quite as exciting as hearing the word *experiment*, and anticipation of the unknown is sure to engage every one of your learners. This is also the perfect step of the process for reviewing what you've already done. We strongly encourage you to go back to the anchor charts you made with your students. Reread them or have students reshare their observations, ask the questions you've written down aloud to reignite thoughts about the topic, and have them talk about their hypotheses again with a partner. This not only activates prior knowledge for your learners, but it also helps to strategically review the steps of the scientific process. Remember, we want students to use the scientific process in many areas of learning, so the more we review it, the better!

STEP 5: DRAW CONCLUSIONS

"The colors changed when . . ." "When I added the vinegar . . ." "When my teacher dropped the apple . . ."

Whew! Take a deep breath, collect your thoughts, and pat yourself on the back for concluding a science experiment with a room full of eager young learners. Seriously, experiments can take a lot out of a teacher. Now that you're ready to move on with the lesson, you get to witness all your students' amazing learning accomplishments. As primary teachers we're constantly doing turn-and-talk activities during our reading and math blocks, but it's just as important to put those skills to use during science lessons. During this step we encourage students to converse among themselves, sharing all they've discovered during the experiment. This puts their speaking and listening skills to use and also allows you to implement observational teaching as you listen in. This is a great opportunity to see who got it and who didn't. We strongly believe that children learn best from each other, so let them talk and watch the peer-to-peer learning happen naturally.

STEP 6: RECORD AND REPORT RESULTS

"I found out that . . ." "I discovered . . ." "I learned . . ."

For a teacher there is nothing more satisfying than seeing your students excited about something you've taught them. Witnessing an "I got it!" moment is so rewarding. It's no secret that in science experiments, results can differ based on the slightest change in variables. This final step of the scientific process allows children to show what they've learned in their own unique way. Allowing students to record and report *their* results, *their* findings, and *their* thoughts about the experiment can be a great way to evaluate individual student accomplishments. And it's the perfect opportunity to celebrate the fact that everybody learns differently.

It's important to remember that this is simply students' first exposure to the scientific process. The process is rich in content and needs to be developed through repeated practice. This isn't a one-and-done approach. The scientific process is the catalyst for the rest of your science curriculum. You will use it to equip children to derive their own answers to questions in future lessons, which in turn helps build creative thinkers and confident kids.

OK, so how do we accomplish all this? Are you wondering what it looked like the first time we introduced the scientific process? What steps did we take? How were the kiddos involved? Our secret tool is a fun little item called the Science Box.

1

CELEBRATE SCIENCE:
WHAT IS A SCIENCE BOX?

Science is about the miracle of the mundane, and children appreciate this best! Every child is a scientist!

—SUSAN BOSAK

Who doesn't love a good celebration? Classroom celebrations can make everything seem magical and engaging. They captivate kids and motivate them to process rigorous content under the umbrella of fun.

While some teachers will go all in on celebrations, others might simply add a few items to their curriculum. It's important to remember that celebrations are not measured by the amount of money you spend, how much time you took, or how Pinterest worthy your photos are. Celebrations are best measured by how they engage your students and create excitement for the learning material. You might spend hours painstakingly producing a complete flop one week only to turn around the next week and throw together a raging success during your lunch break.

Sometimes you might even bring like-minded colleagues along for the planning ride. After all, two brains are better than one, right? Collaborating with friends and teammates allows you to create outside of your grade level's typical lesson-planning session. And if you're wondering whether you have anything to bring to the table, the answer is yes, you do. The best way for teams and friends to work together is to find the ways you complement one another. Maybe you don't consider yourself the most creative person, but your organizational skills are just what your more creative friend needs to help get a celebration up and running.

For us, it all started when Kim wanted to create a Celebrate the Scientist party to help her daughter Megan launch a science curriculum in her second-grade classroom. With the help of her friend Kathleen, a retired educator from Illinois who's always up for fun and ready to share engaging, rigorous content, Kim prepared a special scientist snack and a mystery delivery to celebrate the science journey Megan's students were about to embark on.

To celebrate like a scientist, you must look the part, right? Believe it or not, that idea is exactly how the first Science Box came to be—with a little teamwork from Kim and Kathleen. So, what is the Science Box, and what's in it?

THE FIRST SCIENCE BOX

WHAT'S IN THE BOX?

- A letter from Dr. Science with a call to action
- T-shirt lab coats
- Name badges
- Goggles (we found these at the dollar store)
- Rubber gloves (we found these at the dollar store)

The box itself can be really simple. We used a medium-size plastic storage container with a lid, but really any box will work. You can even use a basic cardboard box! The first box that arrives on your celebration day will include all the PPE—or personal protective equipment—your little scientists will need for your weekly experiments. It will also contain a letter from a fictional character we call Dr. Science, posters outlining the steps of the scientific process, and a shipping label addressed to your classroom. The scientist "lab coat" (a T-shirt) students receive during the celebration is really the highlight. Beyond that, you can pick and choose what you want to put inside. Here are the things we put in our first Scence Box (read on to learn more about each item).

PPE (PERSONAL PROTECTIVE EQUIPMENT)

When you think about scientists and their uniform, the first thing that comes to mind is a lab coat. A simple white T-shirt can easily fit over students' clothes and hang loosely, acting as a lab coat that the children can wear during their weekly mad scientist experiments. This will create anticipation each week as the children put on their gear, and it will signal that it's time to think like a scientist.

You can make the lab coats as simple or as elaborate as you'd like. Remember, the goal is to find things that will engage your learners, protect their clothing, and make them feel like real scientists. Adam prefers to draw details on the T-shirts with a Sharpie. Kim uses spray adhesive to attach ribbon or hem tape, and then she hot glues black buttons along the ribbon line, creating a faux opening in the lab coat. Either way you choose, voila! An instant lab coat that not only looks great but also protects student clothing during some of the messier experiments.

The other items in the PPE collection are used to promote the safety precautions scientists must take. Check your local dollar or discount store for cheap goggles and protective gloves. (Vinyl, nitrile, or thin plastic disposable gloves can be safer alternatives, but if you choose to buy latex gloves, be sure that you don't have any children with latex allergies.) Feel free to add any other items you wish to your PPE. Remember, you can design your boxes to be as simple or as elaborate as your teacher's heart desires!

Being a scientist is an important job. We attach a name tag to each student's new uniform to recognize this important role. Personalizing each lab coat also helps ensure that each child has a coat that was specifically made for them, and it allows children to develop a sense of ownership for their own PPE.

To make the name tags for that first science celebration, Megan took photos of each of her students wearing a fun comb-over style "mad scientist" wig that had originally been purchased at a local party store for a different celebration. Kim then created the name tags using PowerPoint, assigning each child a special employee number (which was just a sequence of random numerals). Megan pinned the name tags to the lab coats using name tag holders from an office supply store. However, there's nothing wrong with just punching a hole and using a safety pin to attach the name tags to the lab coats. These lab coats turned out to be the key to making the students feel like real scientists.

THE SPECIAL DELIVERY

For the special delivery of the Science Box, Megan and Kim enlisted the help of a willing office staff member. They gave her instructions to ensure the delivery would be timed perfectly. And just like that, they had set the stage for magic, anticipation, and wonder. At the same time, they had created an opportunity for engagement and established a platform to ensure comprehension of rigorous content.

When the package arrived at the classroom via the special delivery person, the children gathered in the class meeting area. Although she was aware of the plan, Megan acted as if she was not. Kim had written a fictional return mailing address on the box to make the students think it came from someone really important in the world of science. A simple address written with a Sharpie does the trick, but you could get really fancy with a peel-and-stick label.

A master teacher, Megan led the children in a conversation about the kinds of things that might come from a science laboratory. She asked questions like these: Does anyone know anyone named Dr. Science? Who knows what a laboratory is? What kinds of things come from a laboratory? Do you see any other clues on the shipping label that could help us?

After a conversation full of anticipation and excitement, Megan opened the box to reveal its contents. Inside were lab coats (made from white T-shirts) and other PPE. She carefully pulled each lab coat from the box and called out the name written on the name tag. When each child came to the front of the meeting area, she placed their lab coat over their head and declared them an official scientist. The kids were beyond excited. It was a little loud and a little wild. But isn't that the goal? Teachers with effective classroom management strategies can quickly pull kids back together when necessary. Once all the children had been declared official scientists, a little impromptu fashion show commenced. This all connects back to our belief that to get children to learn—and more importantly, to get them excited about learning—we have to involve them in every possible aspect of the learning journey.

TIME TO CELEBRATE!

So, we've got our PPE and a letter from Dr. Science explaining the fun things that will happen during our school year. The excitement is bubbling. But no celebration is complete without a snack, right? And what better snack than a science-themed one? On a trip to the dollar store, Kim found popsicle molds that were perfect for her test tube juice snack invention. She simply took a pair of scissors and cut out each one individually. You could fill the molds with Kool-Aid, Gatorade, juices, or just colored water—the choices here are endless!

Kim found the plates at a local party store, and they had the perfect lip around the edge to make them look like petri dishes. Kim imagined putting something slimy or gooey—something that screamed "science lab"—on them, so she added Jell-O with a gummy worm to each of the plates to create our petri dish snack. So simple yet effective for our mission—which is to engage our students.

And that's it! The celebration was planned and executed. Results? The children were motivated beyond our expectations and were ready to become real scientists.

ANOTHER APPROACH

Kim told Adam all the details of the prep work, the perfect delivery and execution, and the children's excitement for their Science Box. He announced that he would be doing it the next day. How did he think he could do it that quickly when it took Kim, Kathleen, and Megan several days to pull it all together? Well, because he's Adam, that's how! Remember, as a flies-by-the-seat-of-his-pants type Z to Kim's bullet-points-and-organization type A, Adam can change a lesson on a dime, and he flourishes in chaos. While Kim spent hours securing buttons and ribbon to her lab coat T-shirts, Adam took a Sharpie and drew the details right onto his.

So which way is the right way? Either! Whether you're a Kim or an Adam, the goal is the same. We both succeeded in instilling excitement and anticipation in our learners. We both captivated our kiddos to provide a platform for engagement and learning. Most importantly, the kids won't know the difference between approaches because they'll be too excited to start their science experiments. (But really—a Sharpie!)

2

THE SCIENCE BOX

In the day or two following the celebration, give your students their first assignment as scientists. This will include creating their first weekly Science Box, which you will either strategically place in the classroom or have delivered by your helper from the office. Normally we include the Science Box as part of our Fun Friday celebrations. This means that every Friday, upon arriving in the classroom or after the delivery is made, your kiddos will discover that week's Science Box containing experiments and the materials needed to do them. Call your students together in the meeting area to explore the contents, taking special care to build suspense and excitement for your lesson and experiment. In true scientist fashion, before opening the box, use what you have learned about the beginning stages of the scientific process. Discuss the image on the front of the box, read the words, ask questions, and make a hypothesis about what you think might be inside. No other engagement strategy is needed to spark excitement for what is to come.

Since you'll have already given your students their PPE, pack each week's Science Box with new and interesting items from your STEM stash (more on that soon) in preparation for the activities and experiments you'll do throughout the year. Your box might include:

- A letter from Dr. Science with the concept being explored
- An experiment card with simple steps to conduct the week's experiment

- Recording sheets created by you or from your existing curriculum
- Items from the STEM stash that are needed for the experiment

We also include the simple charts and posters we showed you in the book's introduction that outline the steps of the scientific process. We fill these out as a class during our celebration as we introduce students to science.

DR. SCIENCE LETTER

Each weekly box contains a letter addressed to the class from Dr. Science (the kids will think Dr. Science is real). The letter introduces the procedure for the weekly science experiment. It's a call to action and a request for help from Dr. Science. The letter poses engaging questions about each topic, and it helps spark student interest in the science lesson. We've included an example of one of our letters, but yours could easily be a handwritten letter addressed to your class. However you decide to do it is great! There is no right or wrong way to kick-start the lesson as long as it engages and excites your young scientists.

EXPERIMENT CARD

We include an experiment card for each science activity we perform. The experiment card states simple steps that students follow to complete the experiment. We make sure to include readable text and provide good picture support that will guide all students through the process regardless of their academic skill level. Procedural nonfiction text helps children develop a broader view of nonfiction text, and this is important because teachers use lots of informational text. It's how we teach much of our curriculum. Broadening children's nonfiction text knowledge by showing them the variety of texts available can help them connect the dots. Menus, recipes, maps, directions—these all provide a more inclusive view of nonfiction text. Simple text and picture-driven directions help students develop an understanding of how nonfiction text is used to navigate our daily lives.

RECORDING SHEETS

Recording sheets provide a framework for children to work through content using the scientific method. By using a thoughtful layout, questions, and designated areas for responses, you can help your scientists easily use the scientific method to make hypotheses and record their data in a fun, kid-friendly way. These recording sheets make a great conversation starter at home as well. When children feel involved in the learning process, they retain clearer memories of the events, and this will help them share their experiences at home.

EXPERIMENT SUPPLIES

The final thing to include in each box is all the supplies needed for the experiment. If your supplies are in one location, you won't discover that you left something necessary on the dining room table at home. We detail every item needed to complete each step of the scientific method. This also helps kids believe that Dr. Science really sent this box. When you sell this idea well enough, the kids will buy in. (Don't believe us? Most of the items we've used for experiments were things we already had in our classroom. Some items even had our name or initials written on them—and the kids never questioned it!)

STEM STASH

How often have you thought of doing a STEM activity only to realize you don't have the supplies you need to carry it out? You might just decide to skip it, or you might find yourself headed to a local store after school to find the needed materials. Either way, you'll find yourself facing a lack of time or resources. We know because we've found ourselves in that very place. So let us help you out a bit by suggesting you start your very own STEM stash.

First, decide what materials you use most often in science/STEM experiments. Do you already have some of these materials in your classroom? If so, pull them together and place them into a plastic container labeled with the contents. Next, consider where you might be able to get the materials you still need. Could you ask the parents of your students? Could you send out an email asking colleagues if they have access to any of them? Could you use supply money, write a grant, or find some other way purchase the resources? Finally, once you have all your materials, organize them! Nothing is worse than knowing you have something that you just can't find. We used the plastic shoe boxes that you can find in nearly every department or discount store. You can also keep

some extra storage boxes on hand to allow yourself room to expand your stash as you create more activities.

The ideas are endless. One easy way to build your stash is to add to it as you go. When you do an activity and gather the supplies, start a box for each of those items. Do this each time you do an experiment and continue to add to the stash throughout the year. Just be sure you're checking your stash so you don't start multiple boxes for the same item.

STEM STASH

- Playing cards
- Pipe cleaners
- Toothpicks
- Popsicle sticks
- Tongue depressors
- Play-Doh
- Feathers
- Rubber bands
- Lunch bags
- Plastic cups
- Plastic silverware
- Beans
- Ziploc plastic bags
- Paper plates
- Tape
- Spray bottles
- String
- Yarn
- Straws
- Items for nonstandard measurement
- Rulers
- Linking cubes
- Chopsticks
- Scissors
- Glue
- Crayons
- Pencils
- Markers
- Paper clips
- Index cards
- Aluminum foil
- Spools

THE SCIENCE BOX

INTRODUCING CHILDREN TO THE SCIENTIFIC METHOD

LEARNING FOCUS

The guiding principle for our science curriculum is that each activity we choose applies the scientific method and can be adapted to fit any teaching style or classroom setup. Our first experiment with the Science Box invites students to test the effects of various liquids on gummy bears. However, the effects are not what is important. The purpose of this experiment is to help students develop an understanding of the scientific method and how to apply it in their own learning.

WHAT'S IN THE BOX?

- Dr. Science letter
- Scientific method posters
- Chart paper
- Bag of questions (paper bag with questions on cards)
- Gummy bears
- Water
- Vinegar
- Baking soda
- Small plastic cups
- Labels for cups ("water," "vinegar," "baking soda")
- Directions/experiment card
- Recording sheets

After creating the initial Science Box of PPE, we wanted to send another box. We were eager to send it before the excitement waned, and we also wanted to share the basic premise of our teaching: the scientific method. A variety of experiments can and should be shared with primary-age students. However, not every teacher needs to do the exact same experiments. For our first experiment, we picked an activity that we thought would be engaging and would easily integrate the scientific method. To develop a deeper understanding of it, we wanted to break the scientific method into meaningful chunks that the children could easily digest. To accomplish that, we decided that we needed lessons that would target each step separately. Wow! We figured that could take up a full month of our weekly Science Box. Who could keep an experiment going that long anyway? With all this in mind, we decided to have the Science Box arrive on Monday. It contained all the necessary supplies, charts, and recording sheets. Each day we would cover a different step, and our experiment would culminate on Friday.

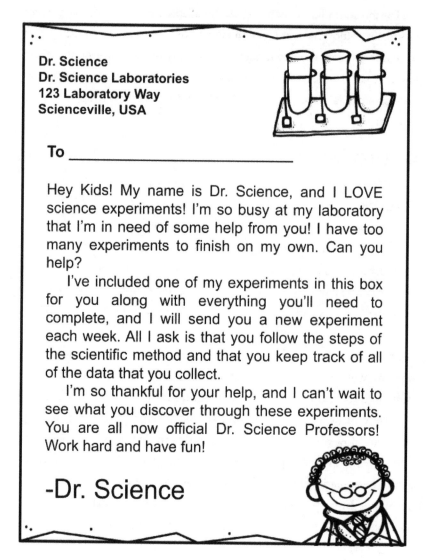

**Dr. Science
Dr. Science Laboratories
123 Laboratory Way
Scienceville, USA**

To _____

Hey Kids! My name is Dr. Science, and I LOVE science experiments! I'm so busy at my laboratory that I'm in need of some help from you! I have too many experiments to finish on my own. Can you help?

I've included one of my experiments in this box for you along with everything you'll need to complete, and I will send you a new experiment each week. All I ask is that you follow the steps of the scientific method and that you keep track of all of the data that you collect.

I'm so thankful for your help, and I can't wait to see what you discover through these experiments. You are all now official Dr. Science Professors! Work hard and have fun!

-Dr. Science

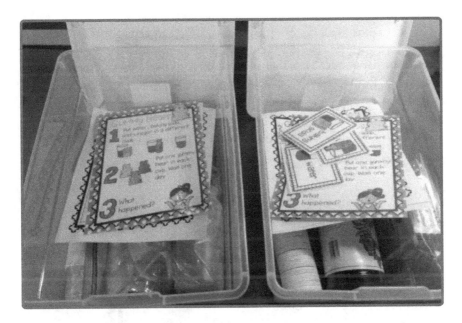

Here is an idea of what the lessons could sound like for each of the days.

DAY 1: SCIENTISTS OBSERVE AND ASK QUESTIONS

"Today I am going to show you how scientists ask questions about things they observe. Sometimes I wonder about things, like how things work or how animals move. So, I ask myself questions like these: Is a bike or a scooter faster? What will a magnet pick up? How much ice cream can I fit onto the cone without it falling off? What would happen to gummy bears if I put them in water? Now it's your turn. You are going to be a scientist! Turn and tell your partner some things that you wonder about."

As the children share question ideas with their partners, write the *appropriate* questions on the chart. Don't call attention to incorrect responses such as statements about preferences or things that aren't questions. Be sure to form their conversations into questions even if they aren't.

"Let's look at all the questions that we have as scientists!"

Read the list of questions that you put on the chart. Reveal the first scientific method posters (*Scientists Make Observations* and *Scientists Ask Questions*) from the Science Box and hang them on the board.

"So, remember, today and every day, scientists always start with questions about their observations."

DAY 2: SCIENTISTS MAKE HYPOTHESES

"Remember yesterday when we said that a scientist asks questions about observations? Today I am going to show you how scientists make a guess, called a hypothesis, to answer their questions. A scientist uses everything they already know to make the hypothesis. Remember how yesterday I was talking about gummy bears and water? My question is this: What would happen to gummy bears if I put them in water, vinegar, and baking soda? So now to make my hypothesis, I'm thinking that the gummy bears will soak up water like a sponge and get bigger. Now it's your turn! You are going to be a scientist! I'm going to pull a question out of my mystery science bag, and I want to see if you can make a hypothesis."

Use the questions in the bag and invite the children to share hypotheses with their elbow partner. Listen to whether the children are making educated guesses (not random guesses about off-topic things), showing they understand.

"Remember, today and every day, good scientists always start with a question about their observations, and then they form a hypothesis by saying what they think will happen."

Review the *Make a Hypothesis* poster from the Science Box to check for understanding and hang it on the board next to the other two posters.

DAY 3: SCIENTISTS CONDUCT EXPERIMENTS

"Remember yesterday when we said that a scientist thinks about a question and makes a hypothesis? Today I am going to show you how scientists conduct an experiment to test their hypothesis. My question was this: What will happen to gummy bears when you put them in plain water, vinegar water, and baking soda water? My hypothesis was that they will get bigger. I can record my hypothesis on my paper. Now it's your turn. You are going to be a scientist! I want you to think about what *you* think each gummy bear is going to look like. Draw pictures to show what you think will happen."

Invite the children to fill out their recording sheet. (We reproduce the hypothesis and the experiment pages back-to-back. If you do the same, children should only complete the one side today and save the other side for later.)

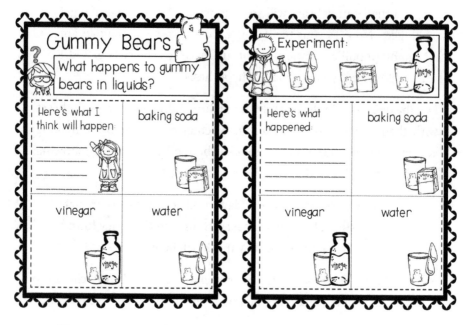

"So now I get to do my experiment! This is the most exciting part!"

Use the experiment card to show the steps and conduct the experiment. You may want to provide each pair of children with the materials to complete this experiment. If so, give each pair three of the included tags to label each of the cups. Whether or not children work in pairs to complete the experiment depends on how much time is allowed, how old your kids are, and how much you are able to manage. For optimal benefit, each pair of children should conduct their own experiment. If not, invite your children to watch and participate through discussion.

"Remember, today and every day, good scientists know we always conduct an experiment to test our hypothesis."

Review the *Conduct an Experiment* poster from the Science Box and check for understanding of the steps a scientist takes while doing experiments. This is a great time for a safety review as well. Hang the poster next to the others on the board.

DAY 4: SCIENTISTS DRAW CONCLUSIONS

"Remember yesterday when we said that after a scientist thinks about the answer to a question and makes a hypothesis, they conduct their experiment? Today I am going to show you how scientists observe and draw conclusions from their experiment. Here is my gummy bear experiment that I conducted yesterday. I can use one of my five senses to collect data—sight! I can look at each gummy bear and observe exactly what happened. Now, on my recording sheet I can draw a picture of the conclusion. I can look at a gummy bear that we didn't put in a liquid and compare to see if it looks different or looks the same."

Here you will model drawing the gummy bears on your paper. Refer to an actual gummy bear from the bag for the standard. Leave the other gummy bears in the liquids. You will use these again.

"Now it's your turn. You are going to be a scientist! I want you to observe what each gummy bear looks like. Turn over your recording sheet. Now on this side, we are going to draw what we observed and conclude about the experiment."

Invite the children to fill out the recording sheet. Encourage discussions between partners or groups about their hypothesis and actual findings from the experiment. This helps solidify the previous steps of the scientific method as they continue working through it.

"Remember, today and every day, good scientists know we always observe and draw conclusions. Today we used one of our five senses—sight!"

Review the *Draw Conclusions* poster from the Science Box to ensure all students are following the steps up to this point. Hang the poster next to the previous ones.

DAY 5: SCIENTISTS RECORD AND REPORT DATA

"Remember yesterday when we said that after a scientist conducts their experiment, they observe what happens and draw a conclusion? Today I am going to show you how scientists record and report data to create a graph. Yesterday I drew a picture on my paper to show what happened to each of the gummy bears. Now I am going to use that data, my drawing, to create a graph to compare each gummy bear. Yesterday when we looked in the cups, the gummy bear in the vinegar had disappeared. It lasted only one day. So, on my graph, I am going to color one box in the vinegar row."

Repeat for each of the other two liquids. If there is still evidence of the bear in the cup, color in a second box. You will continue to develop this graph over the next five days. Demonstrate how to color in the graph for each column. We will continue to develop the graph by recording the observations four more times. If it falls over a weekend, adjust the graph to show the gap in days recording by saying Day 4 instead of Day 2.

"Now it's your turn. You are going to be a scientist! I want you to record and report your data to create a graph."

If you did the experiment together, invite the children to color their graph as you record the data. If they worked in pairs to complete the experiment, invite them to work together to complete the graph based on their own findings.

"Remember, today and every day, good scientists know to always record and report their data after observing findings from the experiment."

Review the *Record and Report Data* poster from the Science Box to conclude the lesson and hang it with the others on the board.

The gummy bear experiment is a perfect way to begin your Science Box journey because it takes very few supplies and minimal setup—and best of all, it includes candy! Your students will love experimenting with floating the bears in different liquids and will eagerly anticipate having some gummy bears as a snack. It's best to start your year of Science Box experiments with simple, easy-to-understand concepts that introduce the scientific method. Creating a special delivery Science Box is one of our favorite parts of teaching science. The arrival of this simple box builds upon the excitement and joy that come with teaching our students STEM subjects and science concepts. So, what comes next?

EXPERIMENTS AND EXPLORATIONS THAT MEET THE STANDARDS

Mary Poppins hit the nail on the head when she said, "In every job that must be done, there is an element of fun." Unfortunately, the "job" that must be done as a teacher can seem so overwhelming that it's sometimes easy to forget about adding in the element of fun. But fun experiments can become the basis of your science instruction and make teaching this subject less of a chore. Sounds easier said than done, right? Well then, let us present a challenge to you. Try to start thinking less about *what* you must teach to ensure your students are meeting a specific standard, and instead think more about *how* you can meet that standard by teaching in the most fun, engaging way possible. When you start with the element of fun, the job you're trying to complete will most likely be accomplished naturally.

With this as our science teacher mindset, we created experiments that meet learning standards, use students' knowledge of the scientific method, and introduce them to content in the most engaging ways possible. Our goal throughout the remainder of this book is to share some of our favorite experiments with you by taking a journey through the NGSS and highlighting key points that can be taught in fun ways that your students won't soon forget! Keep in mind that these experiments may cover multiple standards, and they can easily be adapted across grade levels by adding or changing variables, increasing individual work with the scientific method, and more. We also want you to remember that a lot of the NGSS cover standards have been taught for years, so some things may sound familiar. But we hope that our ideas, new or old, spark inspiration in the minds of all teachers. Try not to get overwhelmed as you look through the standards. You'll surely notice terms and phrases that help you draw on your own prior NGSS teaching knowledge.

Speaking of terms, why do we need so many fancy words to explain what we'll be teaching? In this book, we'll try to translate standards and steps into the same kind of clear, simple language you'll use when conducting experiments with your students.

We'll also be transparent: we aren't going to give an experiment idea for every single standard in every grade level. We have two reasons for that. One, this book would become an encyclopedia, and we know teachers don't have time in their busy lives to read a book that thick. Two, we know there are teachers out there who have their own creative ideas for experiments, and we hope to create a community of learners so you can share those experiments with each other. OK, let's have some fun!

PART I: PHYSICAL SCIENCES

When we think of physical sciences, we think of fun! Well, to be fair, we think all science lessons and units are fun in their own special way. Physical sciences, however, are some of our favorites because they include experiments and explorations that encourage our young learners to think outside the box (no Science Box pun intended) and be creative with their hypotheses and questioning. The reason lies in the fact that experiments in the physical sciences often feature something new to kids or some type of reaction that isn't easily predicted from the materials given. Later in the book we'll talk all about animals, plants, buildings, bridges, and more—all of which include explorations that most of our learners have some background knowledge in. It's easier for young scientists to visualize the outcomes of those types of experiments. But when it comes to the physical sciences, your scientists will be surprised by chemistry, lights, sounds, vibrations, and more.

PUSHES, PULLS, FORCES, AND INTERACTIONS

> **STANDARD:** Motion and Stability—Forces and Interactions
>
> **GRADES:** K-PS2-1
>
> → Plan and investigate to compare the effects of different strengths or different directions of pushes and pulls on the motion of an object.
>
> → Analyze data to determine whether a design solution works as intended to change the speed or direction of an object with a push or a pull.

The experiment ideas in this chapter will center on simple ways to explore pushes, pulls, gravity, motion, and the different ways variables can affect all these. Think ramps, pulleys, magnets, and more! Introducing this standard at the beginning of your school year means you'll lay a foundation your learners can build upon as they experiment on their own with different items in your classroom all year long.

SKI JUMP SCIENCE

LEARNING FOCUS

Designing, testing, and redesigning are three major steps in the engineering process. During this ramp-building activity, students will work through these steps in groups as they use measurement to determine the effectiveness of a ramp. The purpose of this activity is to encourage the children to focus on stabilizing the track, rebuilding, and increasing the launch distance. Gathering supplies is the only prep work required.

WHAT'S IN THE BOX?

- Dr. Science letter
- Hot Wheels tracks and connectors
- Hot Wheels cars
- Tape measures
- Directions/experiment card
- Recording sheets

In 2018 the Winter Olympics in South Korea captivated our kindergarten students. They would come to school each day excited to talk about the events they'd seen on television the night before. This worldwide event sparked conversations, led to creativity in crafts and writing, and gave us an idea for a way to meet one of our science standards. Words like *design*, *speed*, and *direction* were embedded in the language of the standard, so it seemed only natural to create an experiment that involved all of these elements.

Our students were beyond thrilled when they opened a new Science Box and saw the Hot Wheels tracks uncurling and popping out and the cars rolling across the bottom of the box. We tasked our young scientists with designing and engineering a ski jump ramp (Hot Wheels track) that their skier (Hot Wheels car) could ski down without falling off. We split the students into groups of four to five to make this exploration simple—and to ensure we didn't have twenty-five different tracks running around the classroom. The small groups allowed all students to discuss, design, and build within their team. The tape measures added in a bit of friendly competition as groups worked to see who could build a ramp that would launch a skier the farthest.

After receiving a few more directions, the teams went about discussing their plans and drawing up their designs. (This step of the process will help you with another standard that we'll speak more about later in the book: K-2-ETS1-2. That standard says students should be able to develop a simple sketch, drawing, or physical model to illustrate how the shape of an object helps it function as needed to solve a given problem.)

As you may have guessed, some designs were a quick line scribbled across the page, while others were drawn and redrawn as detailed, elaborate structures. No matter the design, this activity gets students working together, participating, and engaging in the learning process.

To make sure students followed the steps of the scientific method even while using Hot Wheels, we encouraged sharing after the groups finished their designs. Each group took a turn explaining their design and offering a hypothesis for how their track would work and how far their skier would launch. This was also an opportunity to check off another step of the process by allowing other students to ask questions of each presenting group. Then it was time for the best part: on your marks, get set, go!

This experiment may look a little different for you if you don't have enough blocks, tracks, or cars for every group to complete it at the same time. To allow plenty of time to complete the experiment, you can add it to one of your station areas for the week so that each group has multiple opportunities to build and try their ramp. It's so fun to watch students test their designs and then make adjustments based on the outcome. We stress to students that the stability of a structure can affect the outcome. With that thought in mind, the children watch closely for the moments when their tracks might waver and adjust that portion of track accordingly. For our activity, we even had a high school volunteer record the experiments and replay them in slow motion so that students could find the exact portion of the track that needed adjustments.

After sending their skier down the ramp, each team measured the distance from the end of the ramp to where their skier stopped and noted it on their recording sheet. Little did they know they were using another step of the scientific method: by measuring, thinking about those measurements, and then using that knowledge to adjust, they were drawing conclusions that could help them make better hypotheses

on their next run. This as an opportunity to teach students that science is an ever-changing experience based on different variables within the experiment.

A later chapter in this book shares ideas for how to use science to make connections across curricula, but this is a perfect preview of one way to do that. In this one experiment, students cover all steps of the scientific method while also writing, speaking, listening, measuring, and comparing measurements. Science, check. ELA, check. Math, check.

RACING TO LEARN: PINEWOOD DERBY TO TEACH SCIENCE CONCEPTS

Guest Scientist: Dr. Lori Elliott (DrLoriElliott.com)

We love ramps and cars so much that we couldn't include just one experiment using them. So we invited our amazing educator friend to share an exploration she did with her students using ramps and cars in a big way.

Have you ever watched a NASCAR race on television or, better yet, attended one? This may or may not be at the top of your list, but you sure can learn a lot about science and math when you watch race car drivers. Car racing may seem loud, dusty, and long, but bringing a version of this sport into the classroom can help us teach speed, force/motion, engineering, measurement, and more.

Drivers . . . start your engines! A Pinewood Derby is the perfect way to recreate car racing and engage students in science standards. Each year I challenged my students to become race car designers and create cars to race during an official Pinewood Derby. The students and parents loved this unit and the special event!

Before we dropped the green flag, I needed to build background knowledge of racing and the scientific principles that make cars move. I began by showing a clip from the Disney movie *Cars*. I set up stations with Hot Wheels cars, toy tracks, and car-related toys for students to explore and have fun with. The excitement would start to build as kids played and experimented. They measured distance, speed, and length of tracks. Students created various car prototypes using different materials and learned the importance of tires and surface materials. We read about NASCAR and other types of racing. On YouTube we watched races, race car driver interviews, and how-to videos about building

Pinewood Derby cars. We even invited local race car drivers to visit our classroom and share their secrets for winning a car race.

I partnered with a local Boy Scout troop leader for our culminating learning experience, the Pinewood Derby. For a minimal cost, I was able to purchase car kits that students could put together in class. I borrowed the actual Pinewood Derby track with all its bells and whistles for our official race day. The scout leader was kind enough to set up the track and help me organize the race schedule.

At the end of the racing unit, we held our very own class Pinewood Derby. We invited parents to join us for food, fun, and lots of racing! Our very generous parent-teacher association donated funds so I could purchase trophies for all the students. We celebrated their hard work as car designers and race car drivers. Above all else, the students discovered how science principles impact everyday things. They could explain with confidence and expertise how speed, force/motion, and engineering work. We definitely learned to race and raced to learn!

ONE DUCK STUCK

LEARNING FOCUS

For this activity students will use a pulley to move an object from one location to another. If you are working with young children, you might find it best to attach the string to the spools prior to the lesson. However, allowing children to attempt to tie the string to the duck will help them internalize the pulley process.

WHAT'S IN THE BOX?

- Dr. Science letter
- Foam board farm scene
- Rubber ducks
- String
- Wooden spools
- Toothpicks
- Directions/experiment card
- Recording sheets

One Duck Stuck by Phyllis Root is a delightful counting story about a duck that gets stuck in the mud. Not only is it a great counting story, but the animal characters also promote teamwork and friendship. These concepts can easily be turned into another lesson for your students. In the end, when the animals work together, they get the duck unstuck! After enjoying this story your students, propose a challenge: How could we help the duck? What if we saw an animal stuck in the mud? How could we help to get it unstuck? Hands will shoot up as the children offer ideas and no doubt segue to personal stories about animals and pets. You know the kind: "I saw a duck once!" "I have a dog that got stuck one time!"

As the class brainstorms, jot down a list of ideas on a chart at the front of the room. This type of experiment is the perfect setting for specific lessons that meet our standards for pushes and pulls using pulleys. Mention those simple words to help spark some ideas for the chart! Prior knowledge of an object or tool can help students make better hypotheses about it, so make sure to do some introductory teaching before you start brainstorming. You can watch a few video clips and read a few nonfiction selections to familiarize students with pulleys and how they work. With the seed planted in students' minds, we like to pretend to have an aha moment: Why not try a pulley? Can a pulley remove something that is stuck in the mud?

To prepare for this experiment, create a farm scene using clip art images of a barn, a grassy area, and a mud puddle. After printing the scene (enough for several kids to share), secure the paper to a piece of foam board.

Have students attach one end of a piece of string to a rubber duck and the other end to a spool. (We found small rubber ducks at a local dollar store and picked up string and wooden spools at a craft supply store.) While it would be easier and save time to prepare the pulleys ahead of the activity, allowing students to use their knowledge to set up the experiment helps develop their scientific and critical thinking skills.

Position the toothpick just outside the muddy area of the farm scene and press it through the image and foam board. Once you've determined how to use the spool, toothpick, and string to create a pulley, place the spool onto the toothpick.

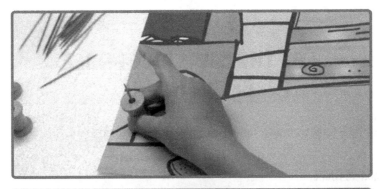

Now you're ready to attempt your duck rescue! Allow the children to slowly turn the spool to tighten the string. They will see how the duck slides across the mud and safely onto land. As students rescue their ducks from the muddy muck, they develop schema that will help them comprehend pulleys in other scenarios.

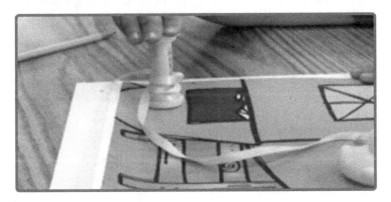

LET THE INVISIBLE FORCE BE WITH YOU

Guest Scientist: LeAnna Wolkis Goldstein, MEd, NBCT

LEARNING FOCUS

This exciting experiment will keep your students engaged while they learn about the invisible force known as a magnetic field. Students will make observations as they carefully pass objects between a paper clip and magnet. This will lead the children to draw conclusions about which objects divert the invisible force and which objects allow the force to pass through. As a result, students will be able to classify things that are magnetic and things that are not.

WHAT'S IN THE BOX?

- Chart of what scientists can do
- Chart paper to collect ideas
- Word cards ("magnet," "magnetic field/force," "attraction," "invisible")
- Coffee can filled with sand or marbles to weigh it down
- Paper clip
- String (tied to the paper clip)
- Tape
- Magnetic wand (taped across can)
- Recording sheets

You'll also want to collect a group of objects to serve as your test subjects. The children will use these to test their hypotheses. Remember to find things that do and do not have metal (iron, nickel, steel, or cobalt). You can choose your own variety, but some good choices are:

- Scissors
- Chalk
- Pencil
- Wooden ruler with metal side strip
- Feather
- Metal button

- Plastic bag
- Paper bag
- Playing card
- Comb

- Forks (magnetic and nonmagnetic)
- Postage stamp

Have you ever noticed the number of children's toys that include magnets? From toy train sets to magnetic gears and marble runs, kids love to explore with magnets. There is a plethora of experiments and explorations readily available to teachers, but we want to share ideas that take simple science to new and exciting places. Our dear friend and creative kindergarten teacher LeAnna had just such an idea.

If you're looking for an experience that will have your kiddos crawling closer to the learning excitement and inquiring about what's going to happen, this one's for you! Through reading aloud, observation, and experiments with magnets, I introduce my students to the idea that forces we cannot see act upon objects.

Now let's set the stage for our inquiry-based science experiment. First, fill a coffee can with sand/marbles to weigh it down and set it in the middle of a table. Tape a magnet wand across the top of the coffee can, leaving one to two inches of the magnet hanging over the edge. Next, tie a string to a large paper clip and tape the other end of the string to the table. Adjust the string so that the paper clip stands up without touching the magnet. This will create the invisible magnetic field. Last, lay the test objects on a plastic tray and place it on the table. Let the magnet magic attraction begin!

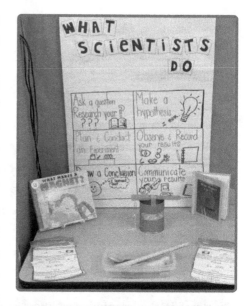

Start the scientific method with your junior scientists by asking a question: "What do you think will happen when we carefully pass the objects between the paper clip and the magnet?" Allow students time to think and make some predictions, and invite them to ask questions. To help encourage student conversation, brainstorm ideas using the sentence stem "I think . . ." For example: "I think the scissors will break the force." Collect students' educated guesses by writing them down on sticky notes and have your super-science smarties peel and stick 'em to the chart paper.

Gather your kiddos in a small group and have them interact with some common objects you've previously collected, or let them find their own items from around the classroom. Tell your junior scientists that they're going to be testing their hypoth-

eses by making predictions and passing different objects between the paper clip and the magnet wand to see if any of the objects will block the invisible force that the magnet creates. Explain that the invisible force is also called a magnetic field and that it is all around the magnet and attracts other magnetic materials. While keeping this in mind, students can explore and make observations as they take turns carefully passing various objects between the paper clip and magnet.

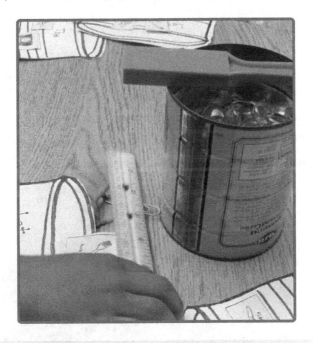

FUN FACT/TEACHER TIP

The paper clip will continue standing until someone passes an iron, nickel, cobalt, or magnetic steel object between it and the magnet.

The magnet fun continues as students test each object, discover what happens to the invisible force, and process their firsthand observations. As students explore, invite them to draw pictures or write words that record which items broke the magnetic field and which allowed the force to pass through.

To extend the learning, I give my students additional opportunities to practice using their scientific vocabulary by sharing their findings with other junior scientists from other classes and even other grade levels. I also have students participate in open-ended explorations that lead them to apply what they learned by independently finding and testing other items in the room, such as nuts, bolts, rings, keys, miniature cars, pipe cleaners, and more.

Some of my favorite things about this simple science activity are that it's easy to set up in a classroom, it won't leave behind a mess, and it will definitely give your junior scientists something to talk about again and again. You'll find this inquiry-based experience fosters opportunities for independent discoveries and hands-on learning. "May the force be with you" as you prepare to take on this engaging experiment with your junior scientists!

VIBRATIONS, SOUNDS, LIGHTS, AND SHADOWS:
WAVES AND THEIR APPLICATIONS

STANDARD: Waves and Their Applications in Technologies for Information Transfer

GRADES: 1-PS4-1, 1-PS4-2, 1-PS4-3, 1-PS4-4

→ Plan and conduct investigations to provide evidence that vibrating materials can make sound and that sound can make materials vibrate.

→ Make observations to construct an evidence-based account that objects in darkness can be seen only when illuminated.

→ Plan and conduct investigations to determine the effect of placing objects made with different materials in the path of a beam of light.

→ Use tools and materials to design and build a device that uses light or sound to solve the problem of communicating over a distance.

One of our favorite ways to connect standards with engagement is through room flips, or transforming our classrooms into environments that create an engaging setting for learning. In this section, we're going to cover two room flips that have given our students learning experiences they will never forget. These transformations take place in the dark, too, which is a perfect way to cover standards that deal with senses. Our groundhog burrow room flip teaches students about lights and shadows as they complete challenges and share information, while our bat cave room flip forces students to use their hearing while learning about vibrations and pitch. Before we get to our room flips, however, let's explore a simple sound experiment that our students love to do again and again.

THE SCIENCE BOX

EGG SHAKE SCIENCE

LEARNING FOCUS

By exploring sound, children can learn how to use one of their five senses to process new information. Students will take turns shaking different eggs to identify the items inside based on the sound they hear. To ensure a smooth lesson, create the sound eggs prior to starting the activity. Choosing items that make different sounds will increase success. Use the number stickers to number each egg, and be sure to select items that most children can identify. This will allow them to use their prior knowledge (vocabulary) to discuss what they are hearing.

WHAT'S IN THE BOX?

- Dr. Science letter
- Plastic eggs
- Number stickers to attach to each egg
- Beans
- Rocks
- Corn kernels
- Googly eyes
- Pennies
- Keys
- Feathers
- Magnetic letters
- Directions/experiment card
- Recording sheets with clip art of the items in the eggs

This may be the simplest of all the experiments and explorations in the whole book. In this activity, students will use prior knowledge to answer questions about sound. Our students always love this one because they get to do something all young kids are good at: making noise! This is an oldie but a goodie—a hands-on sensory experiment that is a perfect candidate for the extra excitement of the Science Box touch.

While we understand every class is different and you may have your own way of doing activities like this, we've always found small groups or stations in our classroom helpful. Just like with ski jump exploration in the previous chapter, this activity allows teachers to model the steps of the experiment when the Science Box arrives so learners have a better understanding of what they'll be doing in the science station that week.

First, read the Dr. Science letter and display the experiment card for all students to see. The picture-based directions make it easy for all learners to get a sense of what the experiment will entail, and the letter from Dr. Science lays it out in more detail. To encourage socialization and discussion among students, pass out a recording sheet to each of them and invite them to talk with a partner about the pictures they see on the sheet.

Students take turns shaking the various eggs to listen for what is inside. As they shake each egg, they use the images on their recording sheet and prior knowledge of the materials to determine what they think might be inside. When they come up with an answer, they write the egg's number on the recording sheet in the box next to the picture of the item they think might be inside.

A word of warning: ensure you make an answer key to keep track of which item is inside which number egg! We've made this mistake before and had to do the experiment alongside our students to get the answers. The answer key helps make this activity run smoothly and encourages self-checking because the students will come to your teacher table to view the key and verify their results. By keeping the key at your table, you can check for understanding and prevent students from simply changing their guess. This also allows you time to ask questions such as "Why do you think those were beans inside that egg?"

WHAT DOES LIGHT LOOK LIKE?

Guest Scientist: Mary Amoson (Sharingkindergarten.com)

LEARNING FOCUS

Explaining rainbows or the visible light spectrum to young learners can be a challenge, especially when you're teaching children who don't understand lights and shadows yet. What is a shadow? Why does a shadow appear sometimes and not other times? It can be downright confusing for little learners. This experiment breaks down some of these concepts for easier understanding.

WHAT'S IN THE BOX?

- Dr. Science letter
- Anchor chart
- Light/magic glasses that break light apart like a prism
- Light sources in your classroom, like lamps and overhead lights
- Directions/experiment card
- Recording sheets

Allow your students to observe a few types of light sources to see what they think light looks like. Encourage them to look at the overhead lights in the room, turn on some flashlights, bring in some lamps, and if

you're feeling brave and your school allows it, bring some candles. Keep it simple and use what you have around your classroom!

Now ask your students a question: What does light look like? While the class discusses this, write down student hypotheses on an anchor chart. Many students will state simple hypotheses such as "light is yellow" or "light is white." They can also write these hypotheses on their recording sheet.

Now, on to the experiment! Start by giving students magic glasses but do *not* let them put the glasses on. The glasses can easily be found online and may also be called diffusing glasses or fire-work glasses.

Turn off all the lights in the classroom except one source that you want to focus on first, such as a flashlight or lamp.

Have students close their eyes and put their glasses on. After counting to three, ask them to open their eyes to see what light looks like. This is a huge learning moment. These fun glasses break light into colors like a prism. You can also use a prism if needed, but the glasses make it easier for each kid to see on their own.

Allow your students time to talk about what colors they see and what colors they don't see. Discussing what colors they don't see is just as important because this will connect to lessons on shadows. Where do they see light? Is it bouncing off locations like waxed floors or glossy walls?

When discussions are complete, review what students observed and then turn on the classroom lights to see if all light looks the same. You can repeat the experiment with as many light sources as you like to see if there are differences or similarities between different types of light.

Refer to the anchor chart and cross off any ideas that are now proven to be misconceptions, such as light being white or yellow. Students can also write down their own results using the right side of the recording sheet. Encourage learners to record all the colors they see: red, orange, yellow, green, blue, indigo, and violet. Use words and pictures with labels to tie into English language arts standards.

We love to follow up science lessons with a book that reinforces what we learned in kid-friendly ways. Two of our favorites for this experiment are *Light and Dark (Why It Works)* by Anna Claybourne and *All About Light (Rookie Read-About Science)* by Lisa Trumbauer.

As we mentioned, your students probably saw red, orange, yellow, green, blue, indigo, and violet in light. (Indigo is there, but it's usually harder to see for little learners.) What colors didn't they see? This question leads to discussions about shadows and the absence of light and is another great way to extend science beyond the lesson. Speaking of shadows, it's time to visit a burrow for our first room flip!

HOORAY FOR GROUNDHOG DAY!

Groundhog Day celebrations are nothing new in primary classrooms; we both did them for years. At the beginning of our careers, this involved just a simple discussion on shadows and hibernation with a little prediction about what Punxsutawney Phil would do. And that was perfectly OK! It wasn't necessarily a holiday that needed much celebration.

But over the years we added more and more science, and we found that a lot of the activities are cross-curricular. Our Groundhog Day celebration now starts a week prior to February 2. We share stories and lessons to help build learning foundations before putting them to use during our celebration day. We create crafts and books, play games, and prepare for our upcoming day of fun!

The reason we recommend completing all these activities prior to the actual Groundhog Day (we finish up on February 1) is because this provides more opportunities for predictions. If students already know whether the groundhog saw his shadow, it takes some of the fun out of the celebration. Send a note home to parents to arrange to have your students show up to school with pajamas, a flashlight, and their favorite stuffed animal. They will be amazed to see their classroom has been transformed into a groundhog burrow, and they'll be excited about learning in this environment.

Now, pay close attention to this next part: *keep it simple*. Repeat that to yourself. While our setup might look elaborate, we keep it as simple as we can. All it takes is black painter's plastic and brown construction paper cut to look like a burlap banner—your kids will be hooked before they even enter the classroom. The painter's plastic (from a big-box hardware store) will be hung to completely block out all light in the classroom, hence the need for the flashlights (and some additional lamps you can borrow or bring in). Pajamas are a fun way to set the hibernation mood, and let's face it—who doesn't love an excuse for a winter PJ party? We truly look forward to this celebration each year, and our past students try take part again when they walk by and see the burrow decor outside our classroom!

The animal science taught on Groundhog Day isn't so much hands-on experiment as investigative approach. Students learn about various animal species and how they adapt to their environment—just

as a groundhog adapts during the winter months. Have your students share what they know about the stuffed animal they brought in. As a class, sort the animals using this recording sheet.

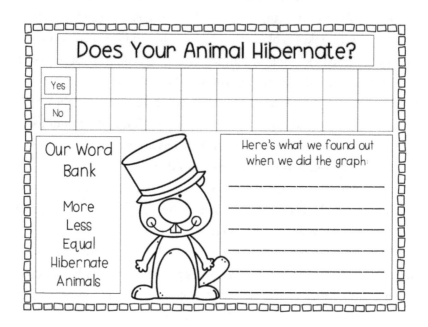

Does Your Animal Hibernate?

Yes									
No									

Our Word Bank

More
Less
Equal
Hibernate
Animals

Here's what we found out when we did the graph:

_____
_____
_____
_____
_____
_____

You could also focus your study specifically on groundhogs. One activity students love is spending a few days reading all the nonfiction information you can provide them about these fun little creatures and then creating a tree map to show everything they've learned. This gives them a chance for some interactive writing as well as an opportunity to share their own knowledge alongside the things they learned from the texts.

Once your students' groundhog knowledge is organized into tree maps, invite each kid to use this information to write their own nonfiction piece about groundhogs. We made a fun groundhog book from a paper bag so each of our students could publish their writing and share with the class!

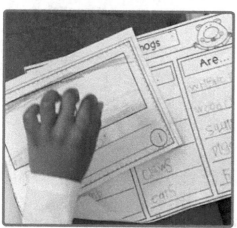

It's easy to incorporate lessons about light and shadows into your blacked-out burrow day. Hang a white sheet from the ceiling with a strategically placed spotlight behind it to create a booth. Inside it, young scientists can physically experience how the absence of light creates shadows. Lead with questions that generate recall of prior knowledge and encourage conversation between students: If we hold up a stapler in front of the light, what shape do you think we'll see on the sheet? What colors will we see on the sheet when we hold up an object behind it? Is there anything in our classroom that we could put behind the sheet that would be hard to guess just by looking at the shadow? Each student gets a turn to stand behind the sheet and hold up their stuffed animal or an object from the classroom while the others try to guess what it is.

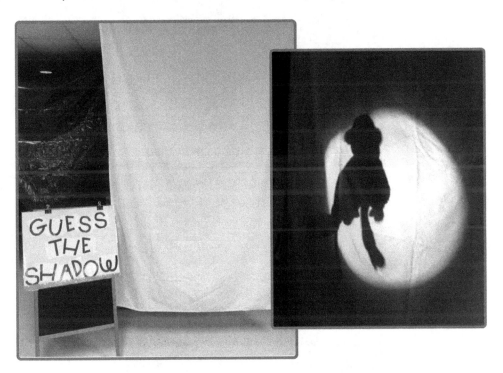

This engaging activity will help you transition to further discussions about the absence of light, shadows, and the shadows students see on the sheet: How do you know that's a monkey behind the sheet? Why can't we see the face of the monkey? What would happen if we turned the monkey around behind the sheet?

Don't want to hang a sheet from the ceiling? You could also use a simple shadow box. To create this box, simply cut a rectangle out of the top out of a copy paper box lid and add a piece of thin parchment paper to fill the space. Then, objects can be placed inside the box. Shine a flashlight onto the object and the shadow will display on the parchment paper.

We end our day in the burrow with yet more questioning—and perhaps the most important question: Will the groundhog see his shadow tomorrow or not? Remember, you're doing this the day before

Groundhog Day so your students can truly make a prediction. The hypothesis step of the scientific method calls for us to make an educated guess, so ask each student to follow their prediction with reasoning. You can prompt this by questioning students: Do recent patterns in our weather make you believe he will or won't see his shadow? You may want to create a chart of students' predictions and hang it in the classroom to be reviewed the following morning after Punxsutawney Phil either sees his shadow or doesn't. You can use an interactive writing lesson to record what ends up happening.

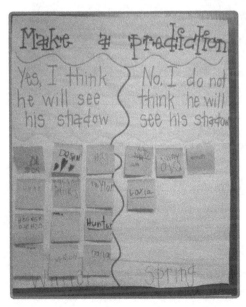

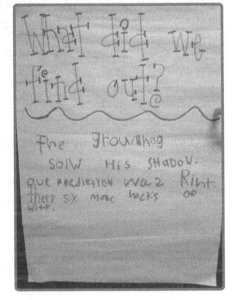

We love to create multiple ways for children to make learning connections, so in addition to our study of weather with groundhogs, we ask our children if they like cold or warm weather best. They create little faces with either a winter hat or a summer hat, and we use these faces to create a graph. It's a little confusing at first, but we connect this chart to our Groundhog Day unit by sharing that if you want warm weather, then you don't want it to be sunny on Groundhog Day. We explain that this is because if Phil blocks the sunlight and sees his shadow, it means six more weeks of winter!

BAT CAVE: VIBRATIONS AND SOUNDS

Each year we also do a room flip for our bat cave unit. This unit was inspired by our amazingly talented friend Holly Ehle (@hollyehle on Instagram), a super passionate and fun kindergarten teacher. This room flip, like the burrow flip, utilizes painter's plastic to create a pitch-black atmosphere that mimics a cave. The day before, send a note home to parents encouraging students to wear all black and bring a flashlight

Our day in the bat cave is full of activities that cover all subject areas.

to school. Most likely, your students will use prior knowledge to make the connection between this request and the bat facts they've learned through stories and lessons leading up to the flip. They'll begin to suspect something special is coming! The anticipation will make them that much more excited.

Adam's wife, Trisha, does an amazing Bat Cave room flip with her second-grade students every year with added lights to help build even more excitement!

CROSS-CURRICULAR CONNECTION

Stellaluna by Janell Cannon

This story is a favorite of teachers and children alike. It's a great way to introduce young learners to the concept of comparing and contrasting while discussing animal science. We read and reread this book throughout our bat unit, but we really focus on the story's details during our bat cave room flip day.

BIRDS VS. BATS

Birds might be a common sight in the sky above your school and home, but you may not typically see bats flying around. Doing a fun sorting activity or Venn diagram can help students compare and contrast birds and bats so that they understand the similarity and real-world connection between them.

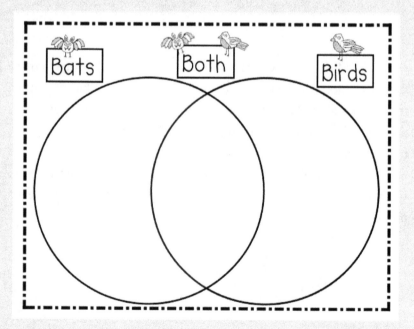

WRITING

It would be easy to pair a non-fiction writing activity with the discussion about birds and bats. But why not let your students' creativity shine? Children might be more engaged if you ask them to write their own stories about birds, bats, or both. Whether you let your students write fact or fiction about these flying creatures is completely up to you—perhaps you can try each approach!

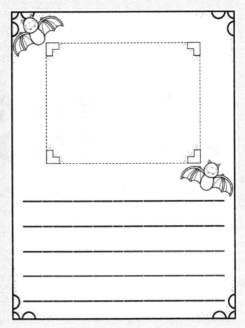

As we continue the day and review what we've learned about echolocation and how bats use sound to "see" in the dark, we play a fun game called Guess That Sound. Our students love this friendly competition, which forces them to work together and use only their sense of hearing (and a bit of background knowledge) to guess sounds they hear via audio clips.

The bat cave is a simple one-day room flip that celebrates everything your students have learned about these fascinating creatures while also tying in multiple subjects and skills.

STRUCTURES AND PROPERTIES OF MATTER

If we're being honest, students' interest might not exactly be piqued when you tell them today's lesson is on structures and properties of matter. But matter *can* be one of the most exciting science topics in our classrooms! Whether or not kids have learned the terms *solid*, *liquid*, and *matter*, all kids have experience with the science of matter, meaning they can quickly tie in their real-world experiences. But it gets better: the experiments we use to teach kids about matter involve food, getting messy, or both! These are the ingredients for an engaging science lesson, no doubt about it.

Let's start with everyone's favorite lesson material: food. We love to bring food into the classroom as much as possible (while being mindful of allergies, of course) to help create excitement, engagement, and interest in lessons. Food is the perfect item to interest all students in matter and to teach them the science behind solids and liquids.

THE SCIENCE BOX

ICE CREAM IN A BAG

LEARNING FOCUS

This fun and tasty activity explores the changing state of matter as it moves from liquid to solid. Little prep is required—you will just need to ensure that you have the required materials and have printed the recipe and corresponding recording sheets. The children will each conduct their own experiment by creating individual bags of ice cream.

WHAT'S IN THE BOX?

- Dr. Science letter
- Ziploc bags (pint size and gallon size)
- Recipe poster that lists ingredients
- Milk
- Sugar
- Vanilla
- Salt
- Directions/experiment card
- Recording sheets

As the old saying goes, "You scream, I scream, we all scream for ice cream!" What kid doesn't love ice cream? Better question: What teacher doesn't love ice cream? It's the perfect treat after recess on a hot day, but you don't have to spend a fortune on the store-bought stuff. Instead, you can turn snack time into science time with this fun exploration. Besides the science fun, your students will get to practice reading an ingredient list and following a recipe. This experiment is also perfect for cross-curricular teaching. The recording sheets and instruction posters offer simple reading prompts for young learners, and the exploration steps include simple measuring skills that students have practiced in math.

Start by brainstorming what your students already know about ice cream, and then pose this question: Do you think we can make our own ice cream? That "scream for ice cream" phrase will certainly come to mind as your students get beyond excited. This question also prompts them to recall prior knowledge of making ice cream at home, visiting an ice cream shop, or seeing videos of how ice cream is made. It's yet another moment when we can level the learning playing field: students who are typically reluctant to speak out in class may be excited to share their experiences with ice cream.

After recording students' hypotheses about whether it's possible to make ice cream in your classroom, share the ingredient list posters that arrived with the Science Box. As you introduce each poster, offer time for thought, commentary, and reflection on the steps. You can also pose new questions for your young scientists to ponder: What will happen to the liquid? Why did we put it in ice? How did it freeze?

ICe CReAM IN A BAG

- One cup of milk (One gallon will make 16 baggies and this is enough for two children to share)
- Two one gallon Ziploc bags for each pair
- One sandwich size Ziploc baggy for each pair of students
- ½ cup salt for each bag
- ¼ teaspoon of vanilla for each bag
- Plastic spoons and paper cups for each child.
- Have children bring in their mittens

Show students how to assemble their ingredients according to the recipe

This last question is the one you'll use to teach the science behind the lesson. Get students to think past the magic happening before their eyes so they can understand the scientific reaction. This is key to developing how they'll think about science in the future. In this case, we explain that the ice and salt are working together to create a reaction that drops the temperature of the bag below freezing, thus turning the liquid into a more solid state of matter.

Of course, no exploration of ice cream would be complete without the chance to taste what you've created. Have you tried making ice cream with your class? Did you explore any variations on the method we shared? If you've never tried an ice cream lesson before, it can be a great way to captivate all your learners and teach them the steps of the scientific method.

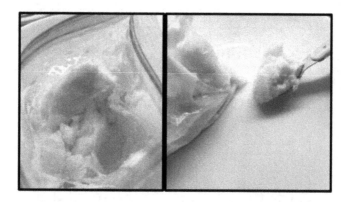

THE SCIENCE BOX

HOMEMADE BUTTER

LEARNING FOCUS

This tried-and-true experiment explores how matter changes from liquid to solid. The hands-on process of making butter allows children to experience a real-world connection to this scientific change. Your only prep work is collecting the materials!

WHAT'S IN THE BOX?

- Dr. Science letter
- Heavy cream
- Jars with lids
- Recording sheets
- Directions/experiment card

- Chart paper for recording hypotheses (may include clip art images that depict someone thinking)

We typically do this experiment during our farm unit at the beginning of the school year, and we've created a simple picture-based hypothesis chart for our students to record their predictions.

There's always room for more food-related science experiments, right? That's the thing about science: it's so easy to make it engaging and exciting with the simple addition of snacks. While most students might use prior knowledge to hypothesize that when you add ice to something it will get colder and possibly freeze, it might be harder for them to visualize creating a solid from a liquid without using ice. We start this experiment by asking a crazy question: "Do you think we can turn a liquid into a solid just by shaking it?"

After all hypotheses are collected and recorded, sit your students in a circle. This activity can easily be done in smaller groups, too. Fill a jar with heavy cream and review what you have learned about liquids. As students take turns shaking the jar and passing it to the next person, we like to read a farm story. You'll most likely be interrupted while reading as your students see the liquid beginning to get clumpy. It really is an amazing sight for young learners who have never experienced it. You'll likely hear "How does that happen?" a million times. The word *magic* might slip out of someone's mouth, creating a perfect

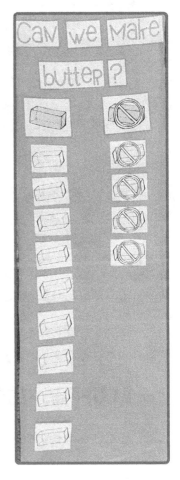

opportunity for you to explain some higher-level science thinking. The illustrated recording sheet we've included with this experiment will help students understand the concept visually. They'll learn that shaking the cream breaks the membranes around the fat particles, allowing them to clump together and leaving the protein and water. That's a mouthful of big words! Now, do we expect all our kindergarten students to walk out of that lesson with knowledge of fat particles and membranes? No, that's not the goal for students at this age level. Our main goal, besides practicing the steps of the scientific method, is to get our students to

Making Butter

1 Put heavy cream in a jar.

2 Shake the jar.

3 What happened?

understand that actions cause reactions. Our hope is that by participating in every step of the experiment—from questioning and hypothesizing to conducting and recording their data—our students will be able to recall information and use it to explain the process in the future.

COFFEE FILTER CHROMATOGRAPHY

Guest Scientist: Shannon Cunningham Lanning, MEd

LEARNING FOCUS

Ask your students this question: "What happens when you mix certain colors together?" They will surely shout out the different color combinations they already know, but the simple answer is that colors come together to make new colors. As the excited shouting winds down, tell your students that in today's experiment, you are going to *separate* colors!

WHAT'S IN THE BOX?

- Markers (for best results, use the Mr. Sketch brand)
- Large coffee filters
- Small cups
- Water
- Pencils

Many of your students have probably experienced the joy and wonder of mixing colors together to create new ones, but what if we could reverse that process? What if we could separate colors? This experiment will build on your students' understanding of colors and inspire a variety of ways for them to turn this activity into something more.

Before conducting the experiment, allow some time for investigative questioning and predicting. Here are some examples of possible questions:

- Will our marker line stay in a neat circle?
- Will the circle stay the same color?
- If the circle changes colors, what colors will there be?
- Will the pencil mark change colors?
- Will the colors disappear?
- Will the water change colors?

To begin the experiment, have each student use a marker to draw a circle on their coffee filter, or you can prep filters ahead of time. The circle should be at least one and a half to two inches in diameter; I recommend making the circle larger rather than smaller. Use a pencil to write the name of the color in the middle of the circle.

Have students fold their coffee filter in half and repeat folding until the filter looks like a slice of pizza. This is also a great opportunity to discuss fractions and symmetry for a science-math connection.

Fill each student's small cup up with a tiny splash of water (it doesn't take much). Have students place their coffee filter into a cup (tip first). Ideally the water level should be *below* the marker line on the filter because the water will naturally travel up and breach the line. Watch closely as the color begins to separate. After approximately three to five minutes, remove the coffee filter from the water. Gently unfold the filter and place it on a paper towel to dry. Watch your students' eyes widen with wonder as they make color observations!

So fun, right? But what's next? How do we make sure the learning sticks? When my class completes an experiment, I explain the *why* or the *how* to give my students a foundation to build on as they continue their scientific journey through other grade levels. For this experiment, I explain that dried pigments within the marker ink dissolve in the water. The water carries these pigments at different rates up the coffee filter, creating the separation of colors that we see. Explain it however your learners will understand it, but make sure you go over the actual process.

Once students have experienced the process, encourage them to repeat it and create unique designs with the coffee filters as they make predictions. Ask them what they could create with their dried coffee filter—perhaps a flower, an insect, or a skirt for a doll. You may consider preparing a coffee filter with a permanent marker to demonstrate the difference between a permanent and a washable marker, too.

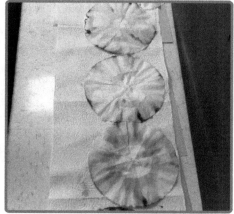

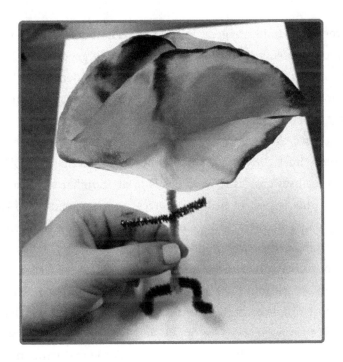

BALLOON GAS SCIENCE

LEARNING FOCUS

In this experiment, students will test whether they can fill a balloon with air without physically blowing into it. Using pop bottles and Pop Rocks candy, the children will see how creating gas can inflate a balloon. The only prep work you need to do is collect the materials!

WHAT'S IN THE BOX?

- Dr. Science letter
- 20 oz bottles of pop
- Pop Rocks

- Balloons
- Directions/experiment card
- Recording sheets

The previous lessons are great introductions and explorations when it comes to discussing solids, liquids, and matter in general. But we can't forget to cover another state of matter with our students: gas! You can have a lot of fun experimenting with gas—its invisibility helps to create even more of that magic feeling around the actual science.

When we ask students what gas is, their answers inevitably fall along these lines: "My mom puts gas in our car to make it go!" "Our lawnmower uses gas!" The word *gas* is pretty familiar to most of our students. This is perfect because it gives us a springboard to launch our discussion of gases. Things really take an exciting turn when we tell our students that they themselves require gas to run. Talk about an attention-grabbing revelation!

Before we get into the experiment or open the week's Science Box, we do some simple breathing exercises and talk about the fact that oxygen is a very important gas for our bodies. We also discuss the fact that we exhale gas with each breath. Then we pull the first item out of our Science Box: a balloon. We ask, "How can we get this balloon to blow up?" Students will no doubt announce that you should blow into it with your mouth. Ah, yes, young scientists! The gas we breathe out will help inflate the balloon, but what if we wanted to blow it up without our mouths? And just like that, you have your students hooked and pondering the solution. This is the perfect time to explore the rest of the Science Box contents.

This experiment is a lot easier to do in small groups (four or fewer) if you're able to get some dedicated parent volunteers to stop by your classroom. It can be accomplished in a whole-group setting, but as the old saying goes, "Involve me and I'll learn." Your students will all be begging for a turn to do something in this experiment. Here are the steps:

1. Open the bottle of pop. (Make sure it isn't shaken up—you don't want to lose the carbonation.)
2. Open the Pop Rocks and pour them into a balloon.

3. Stretch the opening of the balloon over the mouth of the pop bottle.
4. Tip the balloon up so the contents fall into the bottle.

As with any mind-blowing experiment you do, expect some screams of wonder and joy as students see the pop start to fizz and the balloon begin to inflate. Use the process behind this result to revisit their hypotheses and check for understanding that the liquid and solid are working together to create a gas that is inflating the balloon. Good luck trying to squeeze that explanation in over their excitement, though!

As your students fill out data sheets and record the results of the experiment, take time to explain the science behind the reaction. While we understand that complex scientific explanations can sometimes go over the heads of our young learners, we strongly believe that exposure is how they soak in knowledge over time. Constant reminders

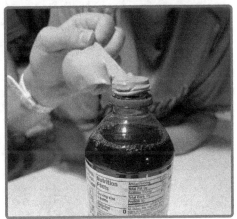

of the why and how of the experiment work to encourage students to look for the explanation behind things they might not understand.

The reaction in this experiment happens because each bit of Pop Rocks candy contains a tiny amount of carbon dioxide gas. To help make a real-world connection to the balloon expanding, remind your students that this is also one of the gasses we breathe out when we exhale. When the solid candy is dropped into the liquid pop, it gets wet and releases tiny bubbles of gas that pop out of the hard shell.

Carbonated drinks like the pop we use in this experiment contain pressurized carbon dioxide. When Pop Rocks are combined with the pop, some of the gas in the soda builds up as tiny bubbles on the candy. As the candy reacts with the pop, more gas is released, and it travels up into the empty space of the balloon. Gases will spread to fill space, and since the balloon is covering the bottle, the gas has nowhere else to go.

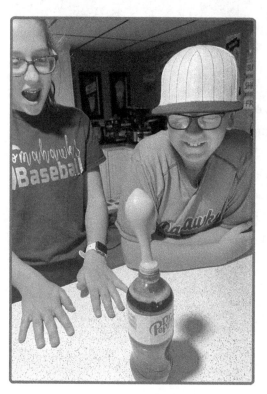

It fills the balloon just as if we were blowing into it.

Imagine the emails of thanks and praise you'll get from parents when their children go home and explain the complexity of this reaction. Try not to imagine the emails you'll get when children go home and dump Pop Rocks into a pop bottle to see the reaction in their own kitchen. Science is supposed to be messy, right?

PART II:
LIFE SCIENCES

Life sciences tend to include experiments and explorations that kids have more prior understanding of. Kids have usually been exposed to animals, plants, and our environment at some point before entering your classroom. What we want to explore in this part of the book is a deeper understanding of how animals, plants, and humans live, grow, and adapt to their environment. Life is fascinating, and viewing different types of lives can be truly eye-opening!

6

PLANTS, ANIMALS, HUMANS, AND WHAT THEY NEED: STRUCTURES AND PROCESSES

STANDARD: From Molecules to Organisms—Structures and Processes

GRADES: K-LS1-1

→ Use observations to describe what plants and animals (including humans) need to survive.

The following experiments are always some of our students' favorites, mainly because anytime the word *animal* is mentioned, primary learners think you've purchased a class pet. And now that we're on the topic of class pets, why not? What better way to teach students what animals need than to let them take care of a real animal? Of course, you'll want to get permission from your administration first. Don't just go buy a class pet and say that Kim Adsit and Adam Peterson told you it was OK. But seriously, how fun would a class pet be for teaching the standards?

THE SCIENCE BOX

DO WHALES GET COLD?

LEARNING FOCUS

In this engaging activity, students explore how animals (whales) adapt to their environment. Prior to the lesson, create the "blubber bags" of Crisco. Be sure you have a way to secure ice just prior to the activity.

WHAT'S IN THE BOX?

- Dr. Science letter
- Two large Ziploc bags
- Two buckets
- One large container of Crisco
- Directions/experiment card
- Recording sheets

Living in the South, Kim is not a fan of cold weather. She prefers to think of sunny days on the beach over cold days when her bones hurt! Cold weather is a real problem for her. But the bigger problem is that most of the kiddos she teaches lack any kind of schema for cold weather, snow, or anything to do with living in a colder climate. Have you ever watched a southern kid who has never seen snow try to make a snowman? It's all the evidence you need of the importance of developing schema *before* embarking on any science experiment. We must ask ourselves what we can do to provide opportunities for our kiddos to use their five senses to *know* colder climates.

We might associate learning about oceans with warmer places. Kim frequently does an ocean study as the last unit of the year because a majority of her students will be visiting beaches and playing in the water during the summer months. They'll witness fish jumping near the beach and explore tide pools. They'll know about jellyfish and crabs. But what about an ocean experience in colder climates? What do the oceans look like there? Are there different animals and plants? Kim has her students explore these questions and more. They know that it's colder in the North and warmer in the South (although it's unclear how much they actually understand). They know about maps and globes. They know that there are many oceans besides the one most of them typically visit. The task is to help them connect the idea that there are colder waters found in other parts of the world.

To do this, kids read a lot and watch video clips about the colder ocean waters and the animals that live there. They explore how they survive, specifically zeroing in on whales. Kim keeps a running list of students' questions so they can look for answers. What do whales eat? How big are whales? Do whales ever leave the cold waters? Sometimes Kim will add to the questions, but if you're patient, you can usually get the kids to ask the questions you're waiting for. Patience can wear thin for teachers, but we need to remember that this questioning step of the scientific method is an opportunity for students with some background knowledge of the subject to think more deeply about it. More importantly, it gives students with little to no background knowledge of the subject an opportunity to listen and learn as they work toward building a hypothesis.

As teachers, we're waiting for one specific question—even if we have to do some directing to get it out: Do whales get cold? Once that question is asked, we can refer to a previous study of forest animals where we talked about what they do when they get cold. By creating a graph of the children's answers to the whale question, we form our hypotheses. Then we set out to answer them through experimentation. Using books and videos, we learn that whales' blubber provides insulation that helps keep them warm. But does blubber really work? Can it really keep whales warm in those icy waters where they swim? We set up our experiment to find out.

Start by putting Crisco inside one of the Ziploc bags. Take the other Ziploc bag and zip the top of it to the top of the bag with the Crisco. Push the second Ziploc bag in so that you make a pocket for the hand. Fill two buckets with ice. Invite the children to put one hand in each of the buckets. Which bucket can you leave your hand in the longest?

Our school's fifth graders actually set up a whale experiment that we were allowed to visit. Talk about luck! We didn't even have to prepare it! Here's what we learned: Crisco acts as an insulator just as blubber does for whales. Insulators slow the transfer of heat from the child's hand (preventing the sensation of cold), allowing them to keep

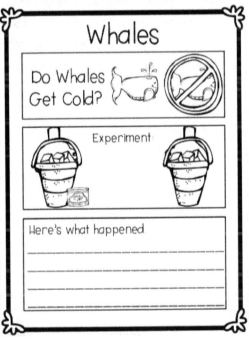

Whales

Do Whales Get Cold?

Experiment

Here's what happened

their hand in the cold water longer. Blubber does for whales' bodies what Crisco does for our hands.

After conducting the experiment and observing what happens when students put their hands into the blubber pockets, analyze the results. Work together to complete the recording sheet and encourage students to try this experiment at home with their parents. What would their parents' hypothesis be? Could they amaze their families just like they themselves were amazed?

THE SCIENCE BOX

DO DUCKS GET WET?

LEARNING FOCUS

This experiment allows children to explore how animal coverings are specific to the needs of a given animal. Applying the water to the oiled feather demonstrates why ducks have feathers and not fur. You can help manage time by taping the feather to the plate prior to the lesson. You may also consider placing the Crisco on various plates at each table for quicker application. Having several spray bottles available will alleviate wait time and keep the activity going.

WHAT'S IN THE BOX?

- Dr. Science letter
- Feathers
- Tape
- Paper plates
- Crisco
- Spray bottles of water
- Directions/experiment card
- Recording sheets

CROSS-CURRICULAR CONNECTION

IN THE RAIN WITH BABY DUCK BY AMY HEST

We love this book! It's a delightful story about a duck family waddling through the rain to the grandparents' home, where they will enjoy a delicious Sunday morning pancake breakfast. As the ducks make their way, the mother and father duck sing with delight. However, Baby Duck doesn't share their enthusiasm; in fact, he's miserable! This sets the scene for an engaging question: Why are the parents so happy while Baby Duck is miserable? Students may have no clue why. They might not make predictions or connections because they lack the nonfiction information required to comprehend the fiction text. Students might not be familiar with ducks and the preening process, making them unable to see that Baby Duck should love the rain just like his parents.

This demonstrates the necessity of determining what nonfiction information students require *before* we share a piece of fiction with them. For this example, we just need students to understand preening. The media we choose is not important. It could be a nonfiction book about ducks or a book about farm animals that contains a section about ducks. It could be a video clip about ducks or some Google search results. The choices are endless, but it's wise to consider students' interests and learning styles.

Ultimately Kim decided to write her own nonfiction book so that she could carefully craft the text to teach very specific information about ducks and the preening process. We want to support the nonfiction features we are learning during our read aloud and reader's workshop, and we want to engage the students in using those features to collect information about ducks.

During our daily read aloud time, Kim makes sure to reread *In the Rain with Baby Duck* as well as share the nonfiction book she wrote. Several times over a few days, she revisits each book with students. Each time they read Kim's book, they search for the nonfiction features they have been learning about. They make a list of the features and the information each feature teaches about ducks. This leads naturally to discussions about the fictional story.

Ducks in the Rain

Do ducks need umbrellas?

Experiment:

Crisco

Here's what happened.

Kim strategically included the direction card for our Science Box experiment as one of the pages in her book. We want our students to know that we can use what we read in the nonfiction text to perform the experiment on the card. After a few days of reading and sharing, the class is ready to conduct the experiment.

As with the experiments you've read about so far, the Science Box will arrive filled with the supplies you need.

To begin, give each student their own recording sheet to record the steps as they follow the scientific method. As you move through these steps, refer to the scientific method charts on display in your room. Begin by asking, "Do ducks need umbrellas?" Each student circles the picture they think best answers the question. Remind them that when they make a hypothesis, they need to be able to support it with information they've learned. Then invite them to turn and share their hypothesis and supporting information with

a partner. This is one of our favorite parts of the process because we can hear what the children learned previously during our read-aloud time. When it's time to start the experiment, read the directions together and display the experiment card for the students to see. The card is carefully crafted so that students will be able to use the pictures to support their reading. Limited text and heavy picture support allow the students to take charge of the process.

Next, the children move to tables laid with the Science Box supplies needed to complete the experiment. While we do a lot of telling and demonstrating throughout our experiments, we know that kids remember best when they're actively involved. To encourage this, pre-tape the feathers to paper plates but have students perform the rest of the steps. Students can use plastic knives to spread the Crisco onto the craft feathers.

Our Science Box also includes several low-cost spray bottles (we get ours at the local dollar store) filled with water, which students share to spray "rain" onto the now oily craft feathers. Do they get a little messy

and maybe too excited about this step of the experiment? Yes! But they're kids, this is kindergarten, and kindergarten is messy! Remember, it's all about experiencing the learning.

After the experiment, review the step in the process that teaches that scientists must observe and collect data. Students can use magnifying glasses to closely study the effects of the water on the oiled feathers. They'll see that it's just like the water on a real duck's feathers. After allowing time for lively discussions among the students, return to the meeting area to share what happened during the experiment. This is the perfect opportunity to finish out the scientific method as students make conclusions and share their findings. On their recording sheet, they can draw pictures, add labels, and write sentences to show their conclusion. Our students keep a dry-erase board at their meeting area to use as a lapboard. Keeping students close together during this step allows you to quickly see what they're doing and redirect as needed.

Wow! To think this all started because we wanted to read one of our favorite children's books with our students. Whenever we pull this book out, we can't keep them quiet! Students all want to share that Baby Duck is a duck and ducks get wet and that's OK because of their feathers. This book opens a new window of opportunity to practice making predictions, text-to-real-world connections, and text-to-text connections. And you can apply this to so many other comprehension strategies.

You can grab Kim's free *Do Ducks Get Wet?* mini unit here. It has the recipe, recording sheet, nonfiction books, and other activities.

MORE DUCK CONNECTION RESOURCES

Little Quack by Lauren Thompson is full of math concepts (particularly composing and decomposing numbers within five) as well as a great story about ducks who are afraid to enter a pond. Students can recall and share what they've learned about ducks' feathers to create a discussion about why it's OK for Little Quack and his siblings to enter the pond.

How fun would it be to include some delightful ducks made from toilet brush scrubbers? After reading the story through a few times, invite five children to hold one duck each. The story will come alive as they role-play and recreate the number combinations, carrying hands-on, active learning across the curriculum to solidify concepts.

"Five Little Ducks" is a great children's song with a friendly melody that students can quickly learn. Its repetitive language and math concept (counting backward from five to zero) will have students singing

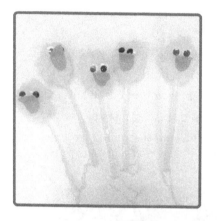

and subtracting in no time. This is also a perfect song to teach or review rhyming words, predictive text, and sequencing. Consider adding this interactive chart into the mix as well. Children will develop concepts of print by tracking the text, and they'll build number sense as they manipulate the velcroed-on ducks and numerals to create various combinations of five.

You can also add the chart as a center activity, which allows children to practice these skills at an independent level or with a small group.

Your own community also offers opportunities to extend your students' learning. You might want to consider inviting a farmer or zookeeper for a visit—maybe they could even bring a real duck! Better yet, if you have a student who lives on a farm, this would be the perfect show-and-share opportunity for that child to teach their friends about ducks.

THE SCIENCE BOX

COLOR-CHANGING FLOWERS

LEARNING FOCUS

In this exploration students will make hypotheses and observe what happens to white flowers when food coloring is added to the water they sit in. This provides a hands-on opportunity for students to learn how the stem of the plant moves the water to the flower. The experiment will take place over a couple of weeks or a period of your choosing. This allows time for the flowers to soak up the colored water and create more vivid colors in the petals.

WHAT'S IN THE BOX?

- Dr. Science letter
- White carnations
- Plastic cups

- Food coloring
- Directions/experiment card
- Recording sheets

Our favorite experiments cause students to stare in awe at wonder at whatever is happening before they take part and learn the science behind the event. When learning about what plants need to survive, we focus on flowers because they're easily accessible and familiar to all of our students. We start this study by bringing a potted flower into the classroom and asking a few of our students to water it. Students inevitably pour the water directly on top of the flower, usually making a mess on the table. They make observations and ask questions, and we soon discover that a majority of our students don't know that flowers absorb water via their root systems. Now, flowers will also

HOW DO FLOWERS GET WATER?

collect water from above using their petals—and the students dumping water on top are actually providing some water to the plant—but with this particular experiment, we're trying to teach the science behind roots.

After cleaning up the water spill, pose this question on chart paper at the front of the room: How do flowers get water?

As with every experiment, we encourage discussions between peers so that we get a variety of answers that use both background knowledge and imaginative guesses. A child using their imagination to create a question can be a powerful step in the process of creating a hypothesis. When a child relies solely on imagination with no background knowledge, the results of an experiment can be even more awe-inspiring to them. Of course, we'll share fiction and nonfiction texts, videos, and other sources of information to help better develop educated guesses, but for this first step we use direct experience as our source of information.

As you move to the hypothesis and experiment steps, present students with three white carnations taken from the Dr. Science delivery. Also in the box are three cups, food coloring, and the paper materials students will need to track their experiment and report their data. Ask them two specific questions:

1. What would happen to these flowers if we just laid them somewhere around our classroom?
2. What would happen to these flowers if we put them in the cups and filled them with water?

After a quick turn-and-talk with a neighbor, hands will start shooting up as students offer hypotheses. Again, this step is important because you're once again calling for students to use their background knowledge of what flowers need. Once you reach a consensus that the flowers will die if not placed in water but will live if they are, spring another question: But how do you know that they'll live in water? Students will likely shout that it's because plants drink water. Ask students another question: But how do we actually know they're drinking the water?

Silence. This is the moment you're hoping for in science lessons. Moments that stump the students. Moments when you can almost hear the wheels turning inside their heads. You see, when it comes to science, the *how* is the most exciting part because it's usually the hardest part for a child to explain.

Tell students that you're going to see if you can catch the flowers drinking the water. Explain that you will add food coloring to the water in each cup. Ask another question: If flowers really do drink the water to grow, will we see them change color?

Every student records their hypothesis, and the experiment begins. Like the ski jump experiment, this one won't be completed in one sitting. You can, however, quickly observe that the flowers don't change color right away. Set them aside to observe and collect data over the next couple of weeks.

Eventually, someone will spot that the white flowers are beginning to show signs that they're drinking the colored water they're sitting in. This is another beautiful science moment: when a simple observation gets everyone excited to learn and turns into a teachable moment full of wonder!

It's time for your budding scientists to put on their PPE and gather their data recording sheets as you take the flowers off the shelf and to the class meeting area. As students start to share their observations, identifying what colors they see showing up in the petals, they will likely notice that some colors changed the flowers to a more vivid hue while others are less noticeable. Yet again, a simple observation opens

up the science floodgates with new information, new hypotheses, and new data to report.

The findings of this experiment help show students that yes, flowers do get water from their root systems and drink it up through their stem to the petals. Sometimes all it takes is the addition of something like food coloring to help explain the science behind the real-world observations students make every day.

FUN FACT

This experiment can easily be adjusted to use other items. In addition to flowers, celery is a fun plant to use. After placing stalks of celery in colored water and letting them soak for a while, remove them and cut the stalks horizontally to expose the veins within. If the celery has soaked long enough and the color is vivid enough, you will be able to see color in the veins. This variation can underscore the concept for some of your more visual learners. While they can see that the flower petals changed color, celery veins may help drive home the fact that the water really did travel up the stem.

THE SCIENCE BOX

MOUSE PAINT

LEARNING FOCUS

Mixing primary colors to form secondary colors is a basic science concept. By mixing colors, children gain a concrete understanding of the process. To prepare for this activity, add a small amount of each of the three colors of gel icing to the paper plates. Arrange the colors as a triangle, leaving space between them. This will provide space for mixing the colors.

WHAT'S IN THE BOX?

- Dr. Science letter
- Paper plates
- Gel icing (creamy frosting will not work)
- Marshmallows
- Directions/experiment Card
- Recording sheets

CROSS-CURRICULAR CONNECTION

MOUSE PAINT BY ELLEN STOLL WALSH

Mouse Paint is a classic story of fun and exploration. As a matter of fact, we think it would be hard to find a classroom or a school media center without a copy of this book. It's a sweet story with a dollop of suspense! At the beginning of the tale, mice decide to play in paint and discover the magic of mixing colors. But painting the paper requires the mice to do some planning. They need to be sure to leave one part white so they can hide from the cat.

We want students to understand the basics of colors prior to reading this book. So, we start at the beginning of the scientific method by asking questions: What are primary colors? What are secondary colors? We use this time to gather information about students' knowledge of colors. With these discussions filling the classroom, we explore how primary colors can be mixed together to make secondary colors. If students have this understanding before reading *Mouse Paint*, they will be able to use prior knowledge to hypothesize what will happen when the mice begin to play in the paint puddles. Remember, we're trying to get students to make educated guesses. We might also use this time to collect some observational assessments of who understood the color-mixing lesson and who didn't. As we get to this part of the text, we want the kids to be up on their knees, leaning in with that "Oh, I know what's about to happen!" feeling. We want science to create readers!

At this point, we decide how to build that schema for mixing colors. Select a video clip of color mixing? Set up a painting center where the kids can mix colors in an exploratory way? Both of these ideas work, but we like to use a prior fiction read aloud as a springboard into schema building. Earlier in the year, during a study on friendship, we read *Little Blue and Little Yellow* by Leo Lionni. It's a sweet story of two color blobs, Little Blue and Little Yellow, who become friends. When they hug, you guessed it: they become green. Although it's simple, it's told in a heartwarming way that students love. After reading this story, we take a cup of blue water and a cup of yellow water and pour them together to show the kiddos green water. We don't talk much about it because we're only planting a seed for this future science experience. The day before we plan to read *Mouse Paint*, we display *Little Blue and Little Yellow* at the front of the room and ask students if they remember this story about our friends. We show them a new cup of green water so they access prior knowledge and recall data from a previous experiment—even though we didn't refer to it as an experiment the first time around.

Then we're ready to introduce *Mouse Paint*. We tell students that in this story, the mice will make green by playing in some paint. We ask, "What colors do you think they'll play in to make green?" As we read, students are excited to see that there's even more paint fun to learn about! Each time we revisit the story, we can look at something different: What happened to the mice's fur? Why did they leave part of the paper white? And of course, what happened when the mice played in the paint?

Now the best part. We are all well equipped to answer our question: Can we make new colors? With our question at hand, our observations recorded, and our hypotheses in place, we set out to conduct an experiment to validate our educated guesses.

Your Science Box delivery for the week will have all the supplies you need. Paper plates, gel icing, and marshmallows—that's it for this crowd-pleasing science experiment. Apply a small dollop of each color of gel icing to a paper plate to form the tips of a triangle. (See the direction card below.) We've also tried the creamy type of frosting, but it was a flop. Stick to gel!

We made this simple direction card to guide the experiment so that students can easily follow. Introducing your students to nonfiction text is part of every curriculum. But how often do you share one of these texts and then just leave it? Pressed for time, it's easy to skip doing the experiments or making the crafts you read about in books. But as the old saying goes, "Less is more"! It's better to meaningfully cover less text than to sprinkle your time across several scanned pieces without ever diving deeper into them. The selected text becomes meaningful not only for this experiment but also for the habits students form as they learn to use text to complete a variety of tasks. Science is a perfect way to develop a love and need for nonfiction text.

Provide each child with a paper plate with gel icing carefully placed in the triangular formation. Each child also needs a marshmallow "mouse." Instruct children to carefully hold the marshmallow mouse in their hands. Have them dip one corner of the marshmallow in the red gel icing and the opposite corner in the blue icing, then tell them to swirl the marshmallow on the white plate. Listen and you will hear squeals of excitement and wonder as the colors mix to form purple. Continue with the experiment by mixing the other colors and watch the magic of engagement unfold before your own eyes.

After completing the experiment, share a picture of a color wheel and ask students to look at their own rather sticky color wheels on their paper plates. You have now entered the world of art! Think of the possibilities for collaboration and cross-curricular learning here. Math, the arts, science, and language arts can all be combined for an engaging learning experience.

We use this printable to replicate our color wheel so that we can save our learning. You can't really save that sticky paper plate too long! If your students are still hungry for more after the experiment is done, you can add this same fun color-mixing activity to a center using a Q-tip or popsicle stick. Have students add two primary colors to their paper, and in another section on the paper, they can mix the colors together.

MORE MOUSE PAINT CONNECTIONS

Here's a pre-K connection: When Kim's daughter Megan moved to pre-K, she knew she wanted to share this experience with her little learners. But the idea of all that icing on one plate sent up a red flag. The experiment would need some modifications to work in her classroom. So, she simply gave each child a plate with two different colors. Each child was able to independently mix their two colors to form a third color. When she listened, what did Megan hear? "I made purple. Red and blue make purple." "I made purple, too." "I had red and yellow. Look, orange." Talk about some major learning happening! With this one small task, she was able to create an experience with language development, sorting, and science all mixed together.

Changing up experiments to allow for different variables is a great way to reinforce the fact that experiments can have different outcomes. Just like Megan used only two colors at a time, you can adjust the types of materials you're using. Whether you use icing, paint, food coloring, or dyed shaving cream, the results will stir up more science conversations among your students.

Invite your art teacher or a local artist into the classroom to expand on the topic and help your young scientists use their color-mixing knowledge to create works of art. Rather than limiting them to a paper plate, you could let them paint away on a canvas or construction paper to create a masterpiece of their own!

SEEDS AND HOW THEY TRAVEL

STANDARD: Ecosystems—Interactions, Energy, and Dynamics

GRADES: 2-LS2-1, 2-LS2-2

→ Plan and investigate to determine whether plants need sunlight and water to grow.

→ Develop a simple model that mimics the function of an animal in dispersing seeds or pollinating plants.

In our constant quest to create lessons and experiments teachers can easily implement, we have yet another set of standards that can be taught using the natural environment around your classroom and school. And educators have been teaching these standards for years! We know we're making that point a lot, but it's simply to help you remember that you're most likely already meeting the NGSS without even thinking about it too much. Remember, our goal is to give you tons of ideas without stressing you out and creating too much extra work for you. We also want to open your eyes to some out of the experiments you've never thought to try before that will have your students engaged and experiencing ecosystems like never before!

TRAVELING SEEDS

LEARNING FOCUS

Plant studies will find a way into most curricula. This activity focuses on how seeds may travel due to forces such as the wind. To prepare for this experiment, secure some socks. You may need to visit your own overflowing sock drawer or ask parents to send extras.

WHAT'S IN THE BOX?

- Dr. Science letter
- One sock per student
- Potting soil
- Winter rye (optional)
- Recording sheets

- Pots or other containers (we use the five-gallon containers from nurseries)
- Directions/experiment card

The Tiny Seed by Eric Carle is a good book to share with your students when learning about how seeds travel. In this classic tale, the wind blows the seeds along, and each seed meets a challenge that keeps it from growing—but the last seed succeeds in becoming a plant. With this experiment, we will answer the question "Do seeds travel?"

Make sure that the socks in your Science Box are large enough to easily slip over your students' shoes and extend up their legs. Each child needs only one sock for this activity.

This experiment is best conducted on a nice spring day because you'll be going outside to explore. It's also best if the weeds have started blooming and your schoolyard is covered with dandelions. Now, we don't usually fix experiments—for us, it is what it is when it comes to science. But we really want students to see that seeds travel, so we also help this one out a bit. Early in the morning on the day of the experiment, we spread some winter rye along the return path, hopeful that some of the seeds might collect onto students' socks.

TRaVeLiNg seeDs

1 Put on a sock OVER one of your shoes.

2 Go for a walk

3 Plant the sock.

Start the activity by rereading the story and thinking about how the seeds traveled. Then display the experiment card and read through the steps. Pass out the socks and invite your learners to place one over one of their shoes. Their excitement will grow when you tell them they're going outside for a nature walk. Make a point to walk through any and all grassy areas, especially those with lots of weeds (don't forget the path with the winter rye you spread, if applicable), and let the kids run around for a bit until you call them back together. Ask if they think they've collected any seeds during their time in the grass and weeds. When they bend down to examine their socks, remind them to be careful not to touch the experiment.

Once you're back in the classroom, "plant" the socks to see if anything will grow. What you plant them in is completely up to you. It could be a pot or container, though a plastic bag will do the trick, too.

Have each child bury their sock in their own container of potting soil labeled with their name. Then have students water them and place them in the classroom for observation. Over the next several days, the kids will water and reexamine the socks to see if anything is growing. If after a few days nothing is happening, you can once again intervene. Spread some winter rye over each of the planted socks and lightly cover it with more potting soil.

Imagine the squeals of delight you'll hear when students notice their seeds have begun to sprout. "See, seeds do travel! We found them on our walk!" Use the recording sheets to write your analyses of the experiment and check your hypotheses. While these sheets are for students to record their thinking, they also provide us with structure that ensures we keep the scientific method front and center. The recording sheets are useful in guiding our conversations as we work through each step. They provide a framework that can easily become part of the learning process during future experiments and explorations.

THE SCIENCE BOX

THE GREAT PUMPKIN CHUCK

LEARNING FOCUS

This activity focuses on the parts of a pumpkin and how they grow. After learning about pumpkins and how their seeds spread through nonfiction text, videos, field trips, etc., your students will help carve a class pumpkin and remove all the parts of the pumpkin they've learned about. This lesson culminates with the excitement of chucking a pumpkin into the air and watching what happens!

WHAT'S IN THE BOX?

- Dr. Science letter
- Pumpkin (if you don't already have one in your classroom)
- Pumpkin cutting/carving tools
- Directions/experiment card
- Recording sheets

The Great Pumpkin Chuck is one of our favorite learning experiences. OK, we know we say that a lot, but we think you'll agree that *experience* rather than *experiment* is the appropriate description of this one. This annual fall event will become legendary as past students tell their younger siblings what to expect when you dig out the first pumpkin-themed decorations and center games. Learning about pumpkins is a rite of passage in almost every classroom, isn't it? Maybe you learn about the parts of a pumpkin or how they grow. Maybe you do pumpkin crafts or play a pumpkin game. We know we do!

Here's a really cool fact: Morton, Illinois, which is only a couple of hours from Adam's hometown, is actually known as the Pumpkin Capital of the World. Needless to say, pumpkins are a big deal in Illinois. Adam's class even takes an annual fall field trip to a local pumpkin farm. It's one of his favorites because the farmers teach students a lot about the crop, which adds to the unit in so many ways. As a parting gift, each class gets a pumpkin to take back to the classroom for decoration, activities, carving, or whatever else they decide to do with it. Who knew a pumpkin could foster so much learning?

When our unit on pumpkins is concluding, it's actually just beginning. Before discarding our class pumpkin, we review our learning about how pumpkins grow. We discuss seeds and what they need to grow into a plant and bear fruit. This builds excitement as students anticipate what's inside the pumpkin. Then it's time to cut the top off so our kiddos can use the scientific method to observe the seeds and pulp inside. We remove some of the seeds, and students take turns feeling the gooeyness of the pulp. Naturally, they have a bunch of questions. We then pose some additional ones:

"Do you think we could grow a pumpkin outside our classroom?"

"How could we spread the seeds outside in the courtyard?"

"Do you think we'll have to dig holes to plant the seeds?"

Students typically answer yes to the last question, so you can really surprise them with your next experiment. Set the stage with these questions: "What do you think will happen to the pumpkin and the seeds if we go outside and chuck the pumpkin up in the air? Will the seeds spread enough that a pumpkin patch might grow outside our classroom?"

Give students time to make their hypotheses. Then conduct the experiment and see what happens! Yep, this is why it's called the Great Pumpkin Chuck. If you have an open outdoor space, line up your budding scientists on one side. Tell them to watch closely to see what happens when the pumpkin hits the ground. They'll have no idea you're going to launch it into the air as high as you can. As teachers, we live for moments like these. So, chuck that pumpkin with force and watch students' amazement as it hits the ground and cracks open.

It can be tough to keep little hands from grabbing at pieces of shell and pulp before you can take a closer look, but do your best to corral your kids. Discuss your findings and compare them to your hypotheses. Students may be surprised to find that the seeds didn't all explode out of the pumpkin and scatter. They may notice that some have fallen out and onto the ground. So, could those seeds actually grow pumpkins right there in the courtyard if you let them be?

Lead your scientists back inside to record and report their data and then make conclusions based on their findings. The real conclusion will come six months later in the spring, however. Did any of the seeds create a new plant? Sadly, you may not get any pumpkins to grow. While

your scientists may be a bit upset about that, your school grounds crew will be happy you didn't start a pumpkin patch in the middle of the courtyard. Want to see more of this experiment in action? Take a look at the video Adam made to highlight all of the pumpkin fun.

If you're wondering, "Can this actually work? Can a pumpkin plant or patch start if I just let the seeds be?" then the answer is yes! Adam's friend Stephanie once left her Halloween pumpkins out on her front porch for too long, and they rotted into her flower beds near the steps. To her surprise she had a pumpkin patch growing the following fall!

CROSS-CURRICULAR CONNECTION

TOO MANY PUMPKINS BY LINDA WHITE

It's important that our young learners begin to connect their own experiences to the texts we read. Many of the activities in our pumpkin unit connect with other subject areas and go perfectly hand in hand with our pumpkin-chuck experiment. After we finish our experiment and conclude whether the seeds will grow where we left them, we read a wonderful story called *Too Many Pumpkins*. It's a classic that's been around for over twenty years, and children are immediately captivated by its illustrations and storyline.

This story features something similar to the pumpkin chuck. The main character, who despises pumpkins, shovels dirt over a bunch of broken ones that landed in her yard after falling off a truck. Much to her despair, this spurs a pumpkin patch to grow right in her front yard. Students love seeing their own experiment spring to life as pumpkin after pumpkin after pumpkin sprouts up in the pages. While the story might be exaggerated, it explains why such a thing is possible. Besides the scientific exploration, we love this book's message of personal growth and kindness. If you haven't already, check it out and read it with your class. They will love the story and make connections between their science experiment and their own life experiences with pumpkins and pumpkin seeds.

There are so many other ways to expand upon a pumpkin unit. But when it comes to making connections across subjects, one of our favorite things to do is look at the number of seeds we can find when we cut a pumpkin open.

The science side of this activity comes into play as we chart the different parts of a pumpkin and practice our labeling skills to show the shell, stem, meat, pulp, and seeds on a diagram. Then we turn to an activity we call pumpkin math. This is a favorite among our students and kindergarten team because of the amount of activities and interaction. We cover four main skills over the course of a few days: estimation, weight, circumference, and skip counting.

PUMPKIN MATH DAY 1: ESTIMATE AND MEASURE THE WEIGHT

We begin this day by discussing what weight is. We share different times and places where we've had to weigh something or where we have been weighed. Most students bring up the doctor's office because they remember stepping on a scale to be weighed. We remind kids that when we estimate, it's very much like a hypothesis in science: it should be an educated guess. So how can we make an educated guess about the weight of our class pumpkin? We borrow the giant doctor's scale from our school nurse and weigh different items from around our classroom. Lots of questions arise that help us connect this activity to the scientific method. We might ask, "Do you think a pumpkin weighs more or less than the crayons?" After everyone has picked up their box of crayons, we let them hold the pumpkin. Then we ask, "Is it heavier or lighter than the crayons?"

We repeat this with familiar items of various weights and chart the differences to better narrow our estimations of the pumpkin's weight. Then we give each student or group of students a die-cut pumpkin to write their estimation on. Regardless of how much you've practiced educated guesses, we can all but guarantee you'll have a student who still writes "1,000 pounds" on their paper pumpkin. That's just another teachable moment, right? After all estimations are taped on our chart at the front of the room, we set the pumpkin on the scale and check its weight. To be honest, we're always surprised at how much lighter or heavier the pumpkin ends up being.

PUMPKIN MATH DAY 2: ESTIMATE AND MEASURE THE CIRCUMFERENCE

This activity involves our pumpkin and a ball of yarn. Pretty simple.

We start by learning what circumference means, and then we measure the circumference of other round objects using pieces of yarn. We cut lengths of yarn that fit perfectly around objects to show how long the string is when stretched straight. Then we display the strings and go over them with students. "The circumference of the globe in our classroom was this long . . ." "The circumference of the tennis ball was this long . . ."

Then we ask students how long they think the yarn needs to be to fit perfectly around our pumpkin. We call each student or group of students up and slowly pull yarn from the ball until they shout, "Stop!" We cut the yarn at that point and send them back to their seat, then we repeat this until everyone has their string cut and ready to measure.

One by one, students take turns stretching their yarn around the pumpkin. We then sort their strings on a sheet of chart paper by pieces that are too short, too long, or equal to the pumpkin's circumference. In thirteen years of doing this experiment, we only had one student who guessed the circumference exactly right. The crazy thing was that same student estimated the weight exactly right as well—*and* he was only off by a few seeds when we estimated the number the pumpkin contained. We'd love to know how he's doing in his math classes now!

To help students make a better educated guess, introduce items they can compare and contrast with. Providing items of varying sizes, such as a globe and a tennis ball, helps produce a standard for comparison. We invite one child to come up and remove yarn from the skein to demonstrate how much they think they'll need to measure the circumference of a given object. To be honest, we always ask a child who we think will err on this side of too short! Regardless, after they pull their yarn off the skein, we use it to measure the pumpkin. After deciding whether it is too long or too short, this becomes the standard. The next

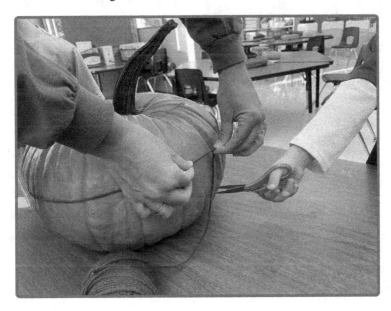

student can now use that information to help them determine if their string needs to be longer or shorter. Repeating this with all of your kids can get you really close to the right length. It's a great lesson in teamwork and using available data.

PUMPKIN MATH DAY 3: ESTIMATE THE NUMBER OF SEEDS

This day connects math and reading. We start by reading a wonderful book called *How Many Seeds in a Pumpkin?* by Margaret McNamara. This tale, like the experiment we will conduct, shares an experience where students are tasked with estimating the number of seeds inside a pumpkin. Don't you just love it when you find the perfect book? This story does a great job of explaining the different variables that could affect the number of seeds in a pumpkin, and it also gives clues to help make a better estimate. We're not giving away those secrets here, though. Go check out the book and read it with your class. You won't be disappointed.

After we read the story and move into our math block, we use our new knowledge to make an educated estimation of how many seeds are inside our class pumpkin. Students write their educated guesses on pieces of pumpkin-shaped paper and tape them to a chart displayed at the front of the room. Then it's time for the best part of pumpkin math: cutting open the pumpkin and digging out the seeds! Each student takes a turn reaching in and grabbing as much pulp and as many seeds as they can. More mess means more fun, right?

After cleaning out the pumpkin, review the previous diagrams where students labeled the parts of the pumpkin. Kids get so excited to finally see the shell, meat, and pulp firsthand. We take the seeds home that evening and bake them so they're dry the next day.

PUMPKIN MATH DAY 4: COUNT THE NUMBER OF SEEDS

To finish our week of pumpkin math activities, we give small groups of students a pile of pumpkin seeds. They get to decide how they want to count them using any of the strategies we have learned in our math units. Some students will line them up and count one by one. Others will count out groups of five or ten in a pile, then use their skip counting strategy to find the total. Some will lay the seeds out in a ten-frame formation to get their number. When all groups have a number, we add them together to find our sum and compare that to our estimations from the previous day.

Throughout the week, each child records their estimations and findings in a pumpkin math book that they get to take home and share with their family. This gives students a sense of ownership in their math lesson and pumpkin exploration, and we always get positive feedback from parents about the excitement their child showed toward math during the week.

Pumpkin math is a simple strategy we created in our kindergarten program around skills we were already covering. Sometimes it isn't a flashy teacher hack that catches the attention of students. Pumpkin math proved to us that a few hands-on activities and a book kids could make their own was the perfect combination to practice math skills.

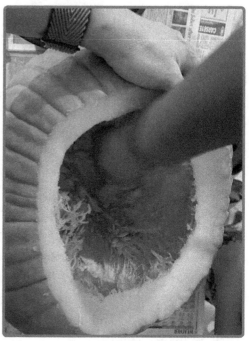

PART III: EARTH'S SYSTEMS

The Earth, the sea, and the air are the concern of every nation. And science, technology, and education can be the ally of every nation.

—JOHN F. KENNEDY

Teaching young scientists about Earth and its systems can seem like a daunting task at first, but it's undeniably one of the most important things we do as science teachers. We all know Earth is changing rapidly and kids need to learn about taking care of our planet. For years, teachers have scheduled Earth lessons in April, with Earth Day in mind. Reduce, reuse, and recycle are common words at that time of year, but why stop there? We want to use science to instill a love of Earth at a young age so that as children grow, so does their understanding of the way Earth, its systems, and the space beyond our planet work.

When children understand the science of our planet, their *why* for taking care of it as adults will have more meaning. If we can teach them about the amazing ways Earth works, from weather patterns and the water cycle to the moon and stars in space, they'll want to learn more about them in the future. Get out the umbrellas and astronaut suits, and let's get learning!

WEATHER AND OUR ENVIRONMENT:
EARTH'S SYSTEMS

STANDARD: Earth's Systems

GRADES: K-ESS2-1, K-ESS2-2

→ Use and share observations of local weather conditions to describe patterns over time.

→ Construct an argument supported by evidence for how plants and animals (including humans) can change the environment to meet their needs.

This section is a prime example of what we've said before: a lot of the science standards cover things teachers have taught for years. If you were to walk into any pre-K or kindergarten classroom (maybe other grades as well), you'd see a weather chart or graph displayed on a wall. Checking, reporting, and graphing the weather is about as common in classrooms as filling in dates on a calendar and singing about the days of the week. And all these go hand in hand as you teach and do experiments with weather patterns throughout the course of your school year.

WATER CYCLE WONDER

A word like *magic* is the only hook you need to capture the attention of your budding scientists. Magic comes up quite a bit when we're teaching students about the water cycle—right before we explain that evaporation is actually a scientific method. When you can't physically show something happening, you can embrace students' wonder and awe as you help them understand what's going on from a scientific standpoint.

Our water cycle unit always starts with one of our favorite songs to help teach the scientific vocabulary. Our dear friend Dr. Jean Feldman, a teacher and an amazingly talented musician, has the perfect song for this introduction. Her fun sing-along called "The Water Cycle" is simple to learn and follows the tune of "Oh My Darling, Clementine." Listen to it with your students at the QR code:

"Evaporation, condensation, precipitation all around. Accumulation, evaporation, the water cycle goes round and round."

We can't think of a better way to get the steps of the water cycle ingrained in the minds of our young learners than hearing this song repeated. Once we have them singing this song on repeat, it's time to dive into the experiments associated with the unit.

THE SCIENCE BOX

WATER CYCLE IN A BAG

LEARNING FOCUS

After you draw the steps of the water cycle on a piece of chart paper, have students use a marker to copy them onto a clear plastic bag. Fill the bags with a small amount of water and a couple of drops of food coloring, then hang them in the window to observe the science behind the water cycle. Over the course of several days, your students will be able to observe and record the process.

WHAT'S IN THE BOX?

- Dr. Science letter
- One Ziploc bag per student
- Permanent markers
- Food coloring
- Directions/experiment card
- Recording sheets

This is a super simple science experiment for all ages of learners.

To begin creating their own water cycle, have each child draw the steps they learned from the introduction song on the outside of their baggie. Encourage your students to draw added details: clouds at the top, some rain or snow on the right side, a puddle on the bottom. Then have your students draw curved arrows pointing from each step of the water cycle to the next.

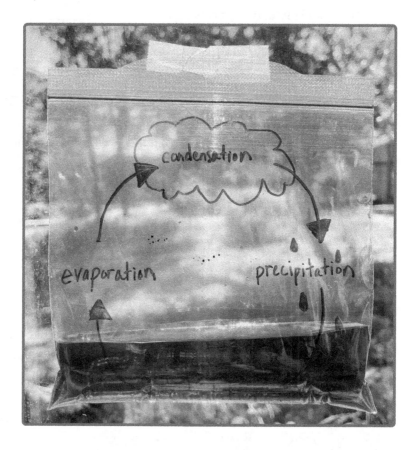

Once they've finished drawing, have your students head to the sink and put a small amount of water in the bag. Add a few drops of blue food coloring to make the water more vibrant (or let each student choose a color to add) and seal the bags. Use tape to hang each bag against one of the classroom windows. Let the experiment begin! Young scientists will be amazed when they come to school and see water droplets collecting at the top of their bags. When they ask how it happened, explain that the water evaporated. Point out that you didn't actually see this happening and that this is because the water turned into vapor.

Students' excitement will grow by leaps and bounds when they see it "raining" inside their baggies. The water droplets dripping down the side will catch their attention the second they walk in the room.

"It's raining down the side of my bag, Mr. P!"

"I can see the precipitation, Mrs. Adsit!"

Success! You've accomplished the task of capturing kids' excitement and imparting knowledge about the water cycle. You can leave the baggies up in the window for a while and see how the cycle continues over time.

FUN FACT

This experiment would fit perfectly after your study on different states of matter. Your students will already know the difference between liquids, solids, and gases, so the water cycle will be easier for them to understand. The sun heats up the water inside the plastic bag, and then the water begins to evaporate and rise into the air as a vapor or gas. The air at the top of the bag then cools the vapor and turns it back into a liquid. As the liquid turns to condensation at the top of the bag, it will fall down the sides as precipitation. This simple model and explanation will help students connect this knowledge to the real world and the water cycle that happens continuously around us.

THE SCIENCE BOX

CLOUD CUPS

LEARNING FOCUS

For this experiment students will simulate condensation by creating a cloud out of shaving cream and rain out of water and food coloring. To save time, consider prefilling the cups halfway with water.

WHAT'S IN THE BOX?

- Dr. Science letter
- Plastic cups
- Food coloring
- Shaving cream
- Directions/experiment card
- Recording sheets

Another scientific phenomenon that children have a hard time grasping is where the precipitation we witness actually comes from. Most children can tell you that it falls from the sky and clouds, but why or how does that happen? Because of our previous lessons on the water cycle, our students already have a concept of the words *evaporation*, *condensation*, and *precipitation*, but the why or how can be still seem mysterious. We can try explaining that as more water condenses, the water droplets within the cloud grow, and when the droplets get too heavy to stay within the cloud, they fall to Earth as rain. But that's an explanation that will go over some students' heads regardless of how well they soaked up the learning during the water cycle lessons. So, to help out our young scientists, Dr. Science delivers another experiment.

To demonstrate the process of water getting too heavy for clouds, give each student a cup of water with a shaving cream "cloud" on top.

Have students use a water dropper to retrieve blue water from another cup and ask them to drop it into the cloud. This step simulates the point in the process of condensation when the droplets get heavier within the cloud.

As the water gets too heavy within the cloud, students will witness the blue "rain" fall from the cloud and spill into the cup of clear water below. This never ceases to elicit shouts of joy, excitement, and wonder from all our scientists!

Have you done this activity with your students? It's perfect to explain the way different variables can affect an experiment. Would the same reaction happen with a different type of shaving cream? Does the type of cup—paper or plastic—make a difference? We have to give a huge shout-out to an amazing teacher in Northern California for sending us these pictures! Joe Kencke is a first-grade teacher who is constantly creating engaging explorations for his young learners, and we love the images he shared with us. Keep up the great work, Joe! Your learners are lucky to have you!

NATURE WALKS

LEARNING FOCUS

For these types of lessons, we typically don't do a full-blown experiment in the classroom. Instead, we take our students out into nature to explore these adaptations in person. Try this around your school and look for some of the following opportunities to spark discussions.

- Look for squirrels. If you see some, explain to students that they bury acorns for food storage. Some of these acorns can get left behind and eventually grow into oak trees. This changes the landscape and creates new plant life and homes for tree-dwelling animals.

- Look for litter. Humans—and animals that dig through trash bins—can have a major effect on the world around them. Explain how litter can be washed away into storm drains where it might enter a body of water inhabited by animals. These adaptations can have negative effects on the body of water and animal life.

- Look for insects. Explain that they interact with our environment in a big way. As plants grow flowers to attract pollinators, bees and other insects help pollinate flowers. Pollinators are critical to balance and maintain healthy ecosystems. A lot of our food crops depend on pollination.

WHAT'S IN THE BOX?

- Dr. Science letter
- Magnifying glasses
- Collection jars/trays
- Rubber gloves
- Trash bags
- Recording sheets

Besides weather patterns, another major part of this section of the NGSS is getting children to learn and understand how humans and animals adapt the environment to meet their needs—and more importantly how those adaptations can affect Earth.

Bringing your students outside to witness these adaptations first-hand can be a very powerful tool in your teaching arsenal. Take a clip-board and blank paper along and let your students create nature walk journals. Or you can use your phone or classroom devices to snap pictures of examples of adaptations and then print them as writing activities for your students. Consider taking along some magnifying glasses to get a closer look.

Depending on where you live, the adaptations your students can witness might be endless and may change as the seasons do.

STARS, PLANETS, AND SPACE!
EARTH'S PLACE IN THE UNIVERSE

> **STANDARD:** Earth's Place in the Universe
>
> **GRADES:** 1-ESS1-1
>
> → Use observations of the sun, moon, and stars to describe patterns that can be predicted.

Children love learning about space—and so do we! Whether students come to you with existing knowledge or a new interest sparked by the activities you've planned, we suggest starting with the stars because kids are familiar with them. Here are a few of the fun activities that have helped us turn our little scientists into astronomers.

ROCK CONSTELLATIONS

LEARNING FOCUS

Space study is found at one or more grade levels in nearly every primary curriculum. This experiment focuses on understanding space, its components, and their importance to Earth. To prepare for this engaging activity, gather some rocks and draw red stars on some and blue stars on others (draw the stars in various sizes). Ensure you have enough rocks for each child to create the stars in the constellation that you are studying.

WHAT'S IN THE BOX?

- Dr. Science letter
- Rocks
- Black construction paper
- Markers

- White crayons
- Directions/experiment card
- Recording sheets

To teach children that stars are different colors and temperatures, we look at images and videos of constellations. We learn how constellations are named, and we ask our students if they've ever seen one in the night sky. To build on this experience and create a fun activity, collect a variety of rocks and draw stars of different colors and sizes on them.

Invite the children to count out the number of stars they want to use to form their own constellation. After counting out their stars, they will carefully drop them onto a sheet of black construction paper that will serve as their night sky.

When all the stars have their place within the galaxy, have students pick them up one at a time and try their best to draw a star where the rock fell.

When all the stars have been drawn, have your young astronomers connect them with lines to create their very own constellation. Each student can then name their constellation and describe its characteristics. Using all the information they've learned through texts and videos about size, color, and temperature, students can write a detailed description of their constellation to share with their fellow astronomers. What a fun way to use nonfiction writing to assess their learned knowledge about stars. The combination of science and artistic creativity can help some of your more reluctant writers come out of their shell because they get to write about something they created on their own.

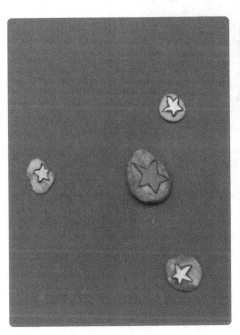

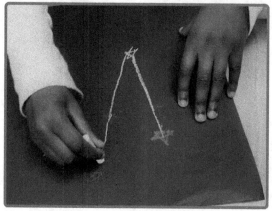

FUN FACT

A constellation family refers to a group of constellations located within the same region of the night sky. They usually take their name from their most important constellation. For added fun, have your students create constellation families with their friends. Maybe their family is based on who they're seated near in class, or maybe they can form families based on similar-looking constellations. You could even task them with naming their constellation family and writing descriptions about it.

THE SCIENCE BOX

TELESCOPE FUN

LEARNING FOCUS

Before beginning this activity, draw constellation patterns (using dots) on small circles that will fit inside a cupcake liner. The children will use pushpins to punch small holes where the dots are, creating constellation patterns.

WHAT'S IN THE BOX?

- Dr. Science letter
- Cupcake liners with constellations
- Paper towel rolls
- Rubber bands
- Pushpins
- Laminated constellation cards
- Directions/experiment card
- Recording sheets

One of our favorite things about teaching is when we can give children an experience in the classroom that they might not get elsewhere due to missed opportunities, financial situations, or other conflicts. Some students will never be afforded the opportunity to visit a real planetarium or even experience an actual telescope, so why not simulate these in the classroom?

After watching videos that offer views of constellations from various high-tech telescopes, we're ready to experience the stars for ourselves. To familiarize students with telescopes, we like to look at images of them on the internet and in nonfiction texts. Then it's time to create our own simple but exciting telescopes!

First, print out diagrams of actual constellations on white paper and cut circles (the size of a cupcake liner) around the images. Glue the papers to the bottom of the cupcake liners. Then use a pin to punch holes wherever the stars appear on the constellation diagrams.

Secure the cupcake liners to a paper towel roll using a rubber band and invite the kiddos to explore the various constellations.

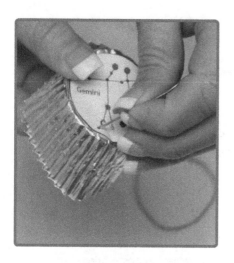 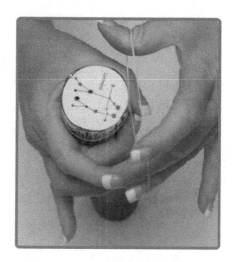

By simply placing the open end of the paper towel roll to their eye and turning the other end toward a light source, students can see the pattern of the stars because of the holes you poked through the paper.

To extend the activity and give students an opportunity to share their explorations, you can also print the constellations onto cardstock and laminate them. Students can look through the cards to find the

constellation that matches the one they discovered through their telescope. They can then record their findings on their recording sheet.

We love using "I can" statements to encourage our young scientists to work independently. These statements also demonstrate the purpose of procedural text as our younger students develop as readers and writers. This is another easy way to level the learning playing field in science and allow all your learners the opportunity to independently read words or interpret pictures.

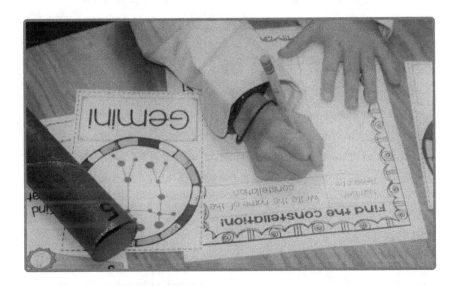

THE SCIENCE BOX

HERE WE GO ROUND THE SUN IN THE SKY

LEARNING FOCUS

This experiment explores space and the ways it affects the earth. In this engaging activity, students will be amazed to discover how a simple tool, a sundial, can be used to tell time. Each child will need to create a sundial. We recommend the simple route: write the numerals 1 to 12 along the rim of a plate, punch a hole in the center, and stick a straw in the hole. Then you just need to wait for a sunny day to complete the activity.

WHAT'S IN THE BOX?

- Dr. Science letter
- Paper plates
- Straws
- Markers

- Pushpins or toothpicks
- Directions/experiment card
- Recording sheets

Now we want to take our young astronomers on a journey to the closest star, the sun. While the sun is commonly described as the brightest or largest star in the sky, it only looks that way because of how close it is to Earth. There are brighter and larger stars out in space; they just don't look like it because they're farther away from Earth. But just like other stars, the sun is a huge ball of gas made of mostly hydrogen but also some helium. OK, where are we going with this, right? Well, those are just some of the facts we discuss with our students as we begin to study the difference between our sun and other stars in our galaxy. The most striking difference our young astronomers spot is obviously the sun's size and brightness compared to other stars. One of the hardest things for them to grasp is that we are constantly moving in orbit around the sun. We hear it every year: "But I don't feel Earth moving." So how can we prove to our students that this is true? Our favorite way is to create simple sundials as an exploration of the movement of the sun.

We begin by showing our students the direction card explaining how to make and use a sundial, and we read the steps of the process together.

We then pose this question to our learners: Do you think the shadow will change position on our sundials? This will hopefully jump-start each student's prior knowledge database and they'll start thinking back to your lessons on light and shadows (like the ones we covered in chapter 4 with our Groundhog Day room flip). Record each student's hypothesis on the board and then start creating your sundials.

TIP

This Dr. Science delivery should come in the morning so you can set the sundials outside at noon.

Once everyone has created their sundial, take them outside and follow Dr. Science's directions for placing the straw so the shadow sits at 12:00. Use pushpins or toothpicks to secure the sundials in the ground. Then head back inside and go about your day having fun and learning.

Make sure you set a timer for 1:00 p.m. and take your scientists back outside to observe the changes. If all goes as planned, your students will be amazed to see that the shadow on the sundial has now moved to the 1:00 position! Show them an analog clock so they can verify their results.

You could repeat this check every hour on the hour and fill out the recording sheets each time. At the end of the day, let your students take their sundials home and encourage them to share their findings with their families!

PROCESSES THAT SHAPE EARTH

STANDARD: Earth Materials and Systems

GRADES: ESS2.A

→ Explore the ways in which wind and water can change the shape of the land

Earth is a pretty magnificent thing. So far, we've taught our students about animals, plant life, weather patterns, and Earth's place among the stars in space. One thing we haven't touched on yet is the way different places on Earth are formed and shaped by water and wind. There are a multitude of books and videos on this subject, and every science book probably covers it at some point, but we've created a simple way for our students to experience Earth-changing processes in action.

THE SCIENCE BOX

EARTH EROSION

LEARNING FOCUS

Because children can easily see the moon in the night sky, a space unit is a great study to include in a curriculum. In this messy yet engaging activity, students explore the effects of meteors on the moon's surface. No prep work is required besides collecting the necessary supplies!

WHAT'S IN THE BOX?

- Dr. Science letter
- Two round cake pans
- Flour
- Cocoa powder

- Marbles
- Spray bottle filled with water
- Directions/experiment card
- Recording sheets

This is a fun exploration to do right after a space unit, where you might have talked about craters on the moon. Your students will most likely be surprised to learn that there are craters on Earth, too. This activity allows your students to see how a crater changes when the forces of water and wind impact it.

When you open the Science Box for this exploration and your students see the flour, cocoa, and cake pans, we can guarantee you they'll

think you're about to bake a cake. Sorry, kids—not today.

First, you need to make the craters on your Earth. Pour flour into the cake pans and spread it evenly across the bottom. Then add a small layer of cocoa powder on top of the flour. Finally, drop marbles from above into the cake pan to create the craters.

This is a great time to tell your students that there are craters all over Earth. In fact, as of 2017 there were 190 confirmed impact craters listed in the Earth Impact Database. You could also pull up images online of different craters around the world just to help give them a sense of how different each crater can be. Then ask, "Can water and wind reshape or fill in the crater we created on our Earth surface?" Students will record a hypothesis about water and one about wind before conducting the experiment.

Now that you have your craters, it's time to see if water or wind can reshape the surface of your mock Earth. Ask the kiddos if they think rain and wind could affect the craters on the moon, too. Begin with the water experiment and then do the wind experiment in the second cake pan. For the water experiment, take your bottle containing water and lightly spray the craters. Stop and observe, then discuss what you're seeing. Some students may want to draw what they see, some may want to talk about it, and some may want to write down their thoughts. Then turn to your next question: Would the wind affect the craters? Have students blow lightly on the craters. Stop and observe again, then let kids talk, draw, and write about what they see.

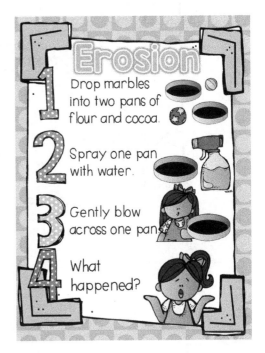

Erosion

1 Drop marbles into two pans of flour and cocoa.

2 Spray one pan with water.

3 Gently blow across one pan.

4 What happened?

Students will record their results on the bottom half of their recording sheet and then discuss their findings with friends.

PART IV: DRAW AND BUILD SOMETHING

ENGINEERING AND DESIGN

It's no secret that kids of all ages love to build things. Whether they're using LEGO pieces, Lincoln Logs, blocks, or other manipulatives, children (and adults) can showcase their creativity while also meeting science standards. Encouraging children to draw or talk about their design before constructing it levels up the learning as well.

STEM (now a household term) is an acronym for science, technology, engineering, and mathematics. It is an interdisciplinary approach to learning where rigorous academic concepts are coupled with real-world problems. Children can use STEM to make connections in a fun and rewarding way in the classroom. This section shares some of our favorite experiments and activities that combine students' design creativity and engineering imagination.

There are five steps in the STEM process:

1. Define the problem and perform research.
2. Design your plan.
3. Build your plan.
4. Test your plan.
5. Improve your plan.

Here are alternative words that describe the steps:

1. Engage
2. Explore
3. Explain
4. Elaborate
5. Evaluate

However you choose to describe STEM, working through the process is the key. When planning your experiences, carefully consider how to include each step.

DRAW AND BUILD SOMETHING:

DESIGNING AND BUILDING

THE SCIENCE BOX

THREE LITTLE PIGS

LEARNING FOCUS

Designing, drawing, and testing are all aspects of the engineering process. Children need to experience situations that provide them with the opportunity to work through that process. In this activity, students will design a house that can withstand the wind. Depending on the size of your class, you may want to create individual baggies of supplies for each child. Include enough gum-drops and toothpicks to build a house. While there isn't an exact number, we put about twelve to eighteen of each. Provide extra supplies in case children need a few more to complete their house.

WHAT'S IN THE BOX?

- Dr. Science letter
- Paper cutout of a pig and wolf head
- Hair dryer
- Toothpicks
- Tape
- Gumdrops
- Ziploc bags
- Directions/experiment card
- Recording sheets

We love using familiar tales as a starting point for science activities. These stories are readily available in most classrooms and boxed curricula as well as in the homes of many children. This accessibility makes it easy for teachers to include bonus activities while covering required texts within their reading curricula. "The Three Little Pigs" is a traditional tale that has been adapted in many different forms and shared with children for ages. It's such a classic that most adults can tell it by heart. Through role-playing and other retelling activities, kids quickly grasp the story line and can reread or retell the tale in their own words. We love using Greg & Steve's music version from their *Playing Favorites* album to add a musical component to the popular role-playing events, too.

After a few days of reading, retelling, and acting out the story, ask students, "What is the problem in this story?" You might get answers claiming the wolf is mean, some of the pigs are lazy, or the houses aren't strong enough. While all are true statements, our goal is to lead the children through our discussion to see that the real-world problem is the pigs need to build a house that can withstand the force of the wind created by the wolf. Helping children connect the real-world problem to the literature makes an amazing segue into connecting real-world problems with STEM solutions.

To begin, have students write the problem on their recording sheet. This can be done through guided writing or as an independent writing activity.

Give each student a baggie with toothpicks, gumdrops, and a paper cutout of a pig. You don't need to include any exact number of toothpicks and gumdrops; just supply enough to allow each child to construct a home for their pig. It helps to have extras on hand for building—and, when it comes to gumdrops, for eating! Let your kids know they are always welcome to ask for more. Once your scientists receive their supplies, ask them to design a house that will sustain the wind and keep their pig safe. Before building, have children draw their plan on

the recording sheet. Let's be honest—this will probably look like a rectangle house with a triangle roof. That is OK. The goal is always to teach the process. Children who establish a firm understanding of the process can apply that process to harder concepts as they age.

Once the houses are drawn, the building can begin. It's in our nature as teachers to be helpers, but resist the temptation to model or jump in and show your kids what to do. It is important to allow time for students to struggle with the activity or—put another way—get frustrated. Just beyond frustration is true learning. Just beyond frustration is joy. Just beyond frustration is independence. Don't rob your students of these just because you want to help.

Once the houses are built, test the design to check the hypothesis. It's so cool to see how some children naturally perform this step during the building process. You may find some of them blowing on their houses to see what happens before they even finish building. Little do they know that *real* wind will be the final test!

For the testing portion, tape a picture of a wolf's head above the mouth of a hair dryer. Have the children bring their houses to the gathering place in the class-room. Once they're all seated on the rug with their houses displayed in front of them, pull out the wolf. You'll hear squeals of laughter as you turn the hair dryer on low and walk around gently blowing it into their hair and faces. When you return to the front of the class, turn the hair dryer on high! Gasps and laughter will continue as students wonder if their houses are strong enough to withstand the wind created by the hair dryer.

Then it's time to test the houses. Have each child bring their house to the front of the room and place it on the floor. Take aim with the wolf turned on high. Did the house remain standing or topple in the wind? Continue testing each house until all students have discovered the strength of their engineering.

You may encounter a scenario where a house doesn't blow over but a pig escapes through the roof, pushed up and out by the wind. If this happens, send the children back to their working spots to think about their designs. How could they improve them? Even if the house withstood the wind, the pig went flying. Students who kept their house

standing and their pig contained should still think of how to ensure their roofs won't allow such trickery in the future. This redesign step is super important. It's hard for kids to accept not getting something right, but we want to empower our learners to see that a faulty design is all part of the process. We want them to see that scientists are constantly testing and redesigning! Invite the children to record their redesigning thoughts next to their original design so they can see their own process on the same recording sheet and share it with their family at home. Encouraging step-by-step thought processes and explanations is a powerful part of the learning process.

This activity makes for a fun-filled week! Drama, art, STEM, and literacy are all front and center as you cover the standards and reach deeper into your understanding of the concepts. However, it's important to remember that in all learning, the real goal is to build schema—to lay a foundation on which future learning can be built. By going through the STEM steps, children are building an understanding of how scientists, engineers, and mathematicians solve problems. This approach to teaching and learning will extend well beyond your own classroom. Students will carry the processes you put in place to other classrooms and into their daily lives.

THE SCIENCE BOX

TOY SOLDIER SUMMIT

LEARNING FOCUS

For this activity students will explore stability and structure as they work in groups to construct a bridge that will hold toy soldiers. You can determine the number of soldiers and length/height of the bridge in advance if you prefer, or you can let students' imaginations run wild and see what they create!

WHAT'S IN THE BOX?

- Dr. Science letter
- Play-Doh
- Craft sticks
- Clothespins
- Toy soldiers
- Directions/experiment card
- Recording sheets

We'll admit that building bridges isn't an original idea for a STEM project. We know teachers everywhere have been doing this since before the term STEM was even coined. It's commonplace to walk into a primary classroom and see students building structures and bridges with blocks. So how do we ensure that we meet STEM qualifications? Easy. Pose a problem and see what kids come up with. Really, that's it!

We created this STEM challenge around the time Disney/Pixar's *Toy Story 4* was released. With the film's characters being the hot topic of young children's conversation and imaginative play, we decided to harness that interest and tie it together with STEM. Toy Soldier Summit challenges groups of students to design and engineer a structure that will hold a given number of toy soldiers and create a path that will get them from point A to point B. Whatever those points are is up to you. Maybe the soldiers are climbing Mount Everest and your students must build a structure from the floor to the table. Or maybe the mission is to get the soldiers over a fiery pit of lava (aka a gap between two of your classroom tables). The customization options for are endless!

We decided to simplify this challenge for our early learners, and we also aimed to do it in the cheapest way possible. A trip to the dollar store will provide everything you need.

Each group of students (we suggest groups of four to five) are given the following materials: one jar of Play-Doh, twenty craft sticks, twenty clothespins, and twenty toy soldiers. You can customize the amount of each item allotted to each group, however.

Recalling our philosophy that engagement is key to reaching all the different students in a classroom, we try our hardest to sell the excitement of every exploration. In this case, it goes a little something like this:

We start by playing the *Toy Story* theme song on our class sound system. In the best toy soldier sergeant voice possible, we call, "Cadets, listen up! Andy's in trouble and he needs our help. Your mission is of utmost importance. We have a team of toy soldiers trapped behind enemy lines that needs extraction!" We have to talk a little louder than normal due to students' giggles and excited conversation. Exactly what we hope for! Kids get hooked into learning, teamwork, and meeting science standards without ever being told this is a lesson.

A gap between student tables and desks makes a perfect "behind enemy lines" area. With very few additional directions (remember, kids must solve a problem), we send students to complete their mission. Immediately our little learners start bouncing ideas off each other for how they could use each piece of equipment. Some talk about building the biggest structure possible while others simply focus on the easiest solution. Once again, this is a science lesson that levels the learning playing field

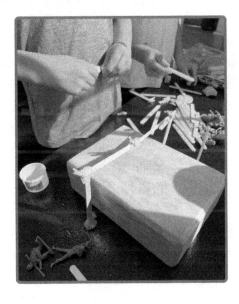

and gives every student an important role in planning and executing the experiment.

We love the differences that evolve in these types of challenges as teams begin building. Sometimes you'll just stop and stare in awe at the design elements your students come up with. It's also fun to see how each team uses the materials in different ways—or doesn't use some of them at all. No, they don't have to use all the items! That's a question that comes up a lot when we're doing these experiments with teachers at workshops. We present the problem and the end goal, but we never dictate how to use the materials. We've seen bridges that have Play-Doh footings and connectors in between popsicle sticks and toothpicks. We've also seen groups lay the toothpicks aside and use only the popsicle sticks flat across the gap, stuck together with Play-Doh. We've seen some structures fall under the weight of one toy soldier, and we've seen others buckle only once all the toy soldiers are on top. In every case of collapse, we are quick to remind students to follow the scientific process. Review the plan, analyze the data, and determine where things went wrong. Do you have to start over? Or do you only need to adjust your plan a little?

Eventually, all our engineers complete the task and successfully build a structure that can hold the weight of all the toy soldiers. The soldiers are rescued! But more importantly, our students are challenged, they rise to that challenge, and we meet standards in a way that's engaging and fun. When we do this with groups of teachers at conferences and workshops, they always have a blast! If we can get adults hooked on STEM challenges with simple materials, just imagine how excited your students will be.

We connected "The Three Little Pigs" and *Toy Story*, and our good friend and fellow kindergarten teacher Hilary Statum did something similar. She took a wonderful story and created a fun STEM activity for her students to explore. We are so excited to share Hilary's amazing multicultural, cross-curricular STEM unit with you!

THE SCIENCE BOX

THE TOOTH FAIRY AND EL RATÓN PÉREZ

Guest Scientist: Hilary Statum (Pencilstopigtails.com)

Let's be honest—the tooth fairy just doesn't get enough airtime. I mean, teeth are falling out of our children's mouths and we hardly mention it! I really noticed what a huge event this is when my oldest daughter had her first wiggly tooth. It was all she could think about, but she didn't know much about the tooth fairy. So, I set out to create a unit specifically for five-year-old kids to research the tooth fairy.

I was surprised to learn that in Spanish-speaking countries, the tooth fairy is actually a mouse. His name is El Ratón Pérez, or El Ratoncito Pérez. I have a large percentage of English-language learners in my classroom. Their grandparents and parents had discussed this little mouse with them at home, but we had never mentioned him in school. It's common to see little "mouse doors" inside a dentist's office in Spanish-speaking countries.

I highly recommend that you check out the book *The Tooth Fairy Meets El Ratón Pérez* by René Colato Laínez. You can also find a story and an entire unit to go along with this study in my Pencils to Pigtails Teachers Pay Teachers store. Neither book is necessary for this activity, however, so feel free to do a little research and create your own presentation, too!

To begin the unit, I like to read these stories and then ask students if anyone has a wiggly tooth. You will *always* have at least one child raise their hand. I excitedly tell them that means that El Ratón Pérez's magical door has probably appeared in the room because he's getting ready to snatch the tooth. We search the classroom, and students are excited to see a little door has appeared in the corner. I use one from the dollhouse section at the craft store, and I stage it with a few other items, such as miniature toothbrushes and even a little bicycle for El Ratón Pérez to ride. None of this is necessary, but if you choose to do it, it adds to the magic and fun!

Next, we compare and contrast the tooth fairy and El Ratón Pérez, write about them, and even apply to be honorary members of their teams. Then we begin our engaging STEM challenge. It's important to follow the steps of STEM: Present the problem first. Then give students time to think. Next, have students draw and write about their plan. Finally, have them test it out. I always save a little time for students to reflect and draw or write about how they would improve their design for next time.

For this STEM challenge, ask the children to build a door that opens and closes. The only materials you need are inexpensive and easy-to-find chenille stems (pipe cleaners), clothespins, and craft sticks. The concept is simple: the chenille stems help hold the craft sticks together to form the door. Students can also bend the stems to make a door that will open and shut. Some students will use the clothespins in their designs. It's so fun to see what the children come up with. You'll probably be able to hear a pin drop as they work on this!

Students get to eventually take the door home so that El Ratón Pérez can visit them the next time they lose a tooth. I always send a note home to parents that describes what the children are learning about, and I encourage them to play along

if they want. For example, I tell parents that the next time their child loses a tooth, they could leave a note that says "From your amigos, the tooth fairy & El Ratón Pérez."

WHO SANK THE BOAT?

LEARNING FOCUS

In this experiment students will explore the effects of adding weight to a floating object. To prepare for this activity, you will need to tape pennies to the backs of laminated animal cards and have a tub of water ready.

WHAT'S IN THE BOX?

- Dr. Science letter
- Foil
- Laminated animal cards (cow, pig, donkey, sheep, mouse)
- Pennies

- Gutter sets or container for water
- Directions/experiment card
- Recording sheets

Who Sank the Boat? by Pamela Allen is a delightful children's story about how weight affects an object's ability to float or sink. Have you ever floated a pumpkin with your kiddos? This is one of our favorite observational experiments. Just ask them if they think the pumpkin will float or sink. Overwhelmingly they'll think the pumpkin will sink! Young children lack the schema to compare and understand the weight of an object and the water it displaces. You can spend some time floating and sinking all types of objects, exploring and sorting as you go. Kids can spot patterns through trial-and-error experiences. When it's time to share this story, students will already have some ideas about objects that float and sink. We like to share the tale many times over the course of a week. When Friday comes and your Science Box is delivered, students will be more than ready to begin putting their week of learning to the test.

Print out several sets of clip art animals mentioned in the story. After laminating the animals, tape pennies to the backs, putting the most pennies on the heaviest animal and the fewest pennies on the lightest animal.

Make some troughs out of gutter material from a local hardware store. We love how easy these are to store and how they don't take up a lot of room.

Give each student one piece of aluminum foil and ask them to make a boat that can hold all the animals from the story. Be sure to keep extra foil on hand—you're going to need it once the crumpled balls of foil start bobbing!

The rest is up to your students. Each student gets a set of animals and is asked to use their knowledge of the text to sequence the animals as they appeared in the story. As an added hint, we like to remind them to look on the back and take note of each animal's weight.

As students retell the story, they add the animals to the boat. The boats *will* tip over. Redesigning and rebuilding is all part of the process.

Encourage your students to try various formations of foil and create alternative solutions that will help their designs stay afloat. Observing their peers' designs can help expand their learning. Say, "Look around at your friends. What did they do differently? Are their boats floating? What else could you try? Why do you think the boat sank?"

While it's hard to not jump in and show them how to build a successful boat, it's so important to resist that urge. Remember, true learning often follows frustration. Support and encourage your students through questioning, redirection, and peer discussions. Modeling good questions will lead to students asking questions of themselves.

We use forms like the ones below for the kiddos to record the process. Provide time for this both before and after building the boat. When students are away from the water, they'll feel less frustrated. The first time we tried this, our papers got soaked and had to be trashed.

After the children have successfully floated their boats with all the animals from the story, try an instant math lesson by inviting them to float their cows. Ask them how many pennies are taped to the cow. Then have them look at their other animals. What two animals can they put in the boat to precisely replace the cow's weight? Continue to pose other questions that involve combining animals to create equal weights.

You've instantly created a brand-new connection between the literature, the science process, and math skills!

While it's exciting to see kids figure out those problems, how exciting is it when they pose their own questions? One of our kids asked if we had any extra pennies in the classroom, and we were so glad that we did. The kids set off with the jar of pennies to see how many their boats could hold. All around the classroom, we overheard conversations that included terms from our unit and the text. Students counted the pennies as they filled their boats until the water spilled in over the edges and tipped their foil masterpieces. Then we got out our ten-frame work mats and counted the pennies onto the frames, writing our numerals on a chart. This led to placing other items into the boats. Would the boat hold more pennies or more paper clips? In the week following our initial boat experiment, we placed the trough in our exploration center and left further investigation up to the students. Long after the actual lesson took place, the children were still weighing, counting, and comparing the objects on their own. While students may not be able to verbalize all the scientific concepts involved, they're developing valuable schema that will be stored in their brains for later retrieval.

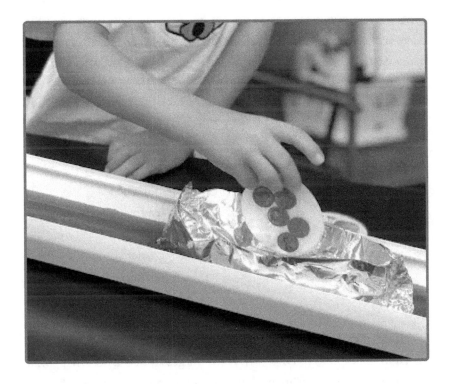

BUILDING SHELTER FOR PIRATE TREASURE

Guest Scientist: Kimberly Jordano (@kinderbykim)

LEARNING FOCUS

Every day we take measures to protect our skin and belongings from the dangers of ultraviolet rays. This experiment allows children the opportunity to design and build structures that provide sun protection. A few weeks prior to this activity, send a letter home to parents requesting materials. This will give families ample time to contribute.

WHAT'S IN THE BOX?

- Dr. Science letter
- Paper pirate and treasure chest for coloring
- Crayons/colored pencils/ markers
- Toilet paper rolls
- Glue
- Hot glue
- UV-sensitive beads
- Household materials (cereal boxes, paper plates, foil, etc.)
- Thermometers
- Directions/experiment card
- Designing sheets

We decided that we couldn't end this book without an experiment dedicated to the captain of DBC, Mr. Dave Burgess himself. So, what could be better than an experiment that centers around a pirate? For this, we reached out to a friend of ours who lives near the beach and has access to fun-in-the-sun experiments no matter the season. Here's to you, Dave! Let's save the pirate!

NGSS K-PS3-1 challenges students and teachers to create a structure that will reduce the effect of the sun's rays on Earth's surface. This seems like a challenge indeed when working with young learners, but challenges are what science is all about. While discussing the challenge, I ask students the following essential questions:

- What can we observe about the sun?
- What is the effect of sunlight on Earth's surface?
- How can we reduce the warming effect of sunlight?

Almost immediately my students pull from their background knowledge (being at the beach and out in the sun, for example) and begin sharing ideas for structures they could build to create shade. To make this a true problem-solving exploration, I avoid prompting them with *what* to build. Instead, I present the problem and give them access to materials to solve it. To help with the building supplies, I ask families to donate household items such as cereal boxes, cups, paper plates, foil, construction paper, tape, etc. I also previously purchased durable thermometers (from Lakeshore Learning) and UV-sensitive beads (from Amazon). To stress the design process of STEM, I print out a design page to give to each student.

To kick-start the children's engineering mindset and drum up some excitement and engagement, I create a PowerPoint that tells a story about pirates who found a very special treasure with magical powers. The only problem is the treasure cannot get hot. The special treasure must be kept away from the direct heat of the sun or its magical powers will disappear.

Following the PowerPoint, invite children to draw a structure that would shelter their pirate's treasure and keep it from the heating effects of the sun.

Next, give each child a pirate with a treasure chest to color and glue around a toilet paper roll. When they're finished, hot glue the UV-sensitive beads on each student's treasure chest. These beads work beautifully to show children how quickly the sun can affect a surface: when placed in the sun, they change color rapidly from white to purple, pink, and orange.

Have students partner up, go over their design plans together, and build a structure using the given materials. This is a great opportunity for conversation between students because they get to explain their design to a friend before testing it.

The next day, children can take turns placing their structures (along with the pirates and treasure chests) in the sun. Give each pair of students a thermometer so they can evaluate whether their shelter actually keeps the pirate's treasure out of the sun and cooler. If it does not, give students time to reflect and make changes to their design.

When the exploration is complete, students can reflect on what they learned and how they could apply this knowledge to different situations. You can prompt them with questions like these: When you're at the beach or pool, what do you use to stay cool and out of the sun? At a sporting event, why do you see pop-up canopies? Do you have any ideas for how to keep the sun off you in your backyard? When children can learn through familiar, real-life situations, the learning seems to stick.

Like we mentioned before, we know that STEM education is nothing new. Challenges that encourage creative thinking have been around for years. We hope the ideas shared in this section—and throughout the whole book—remind you of a forgotten experiment you might have done as a student or even as a teacher. We'd love to see the challenges you create for your students! Share them on social media and be sure to tag @kindergals and @teacherslearn2.

PART V: BRINGING IT ALL TOGETHER

You've nearly made it to the end! Knowing that always motivates us when we read a book, so we thought we'd share the feeling. In our classrooms, science doesn't stop until the end of the school year, but we obviously can't include every single activity, exploration, or experiment in this book. So, although we'd love to keep sharing, we've come to the end of our Science Box journey together. Or have we? We thought we'd end the book with one more example of how we bring science into all the other subjects. Think you've seen some pretty cool activities and explorations so far? Buckle up, we're taking off on one last experience that makes for an exciting end to the school year!

LEAVING (AND LEARNING) ON A JET PLANE

HAWAIIAN VACATION!

One of our favorite kindergarten units is our week-long Hawaiian "vacation" at the end of the year. It's been a tradition at Adam's school since the '80s and has grown over the years thanks to the creative work done by him and his team. So many areas of learning are tied into this one unit, from social studies and math to reading and writing—and of course plenty of science. It's an unforgettable way to end our kindergarten year. (Really! Eighth-grade students talk about their kindergarten Hawaii unit in their valedictorian speeches at graduation every year.) So, what exactly does this unit look like, and what types of science activities does it include? Before we dive in, let's make a note: if you're a teacher in Hawaii—or just want to learn about other places—this unit doesn't have to be about Hawaii. The following ideas could be adapted for an imaginary trip to any location!

PREFLIGHT CROSS-CURRICULAR CHECK

We start by discussing travel and transportation as well as landforms and bodies of water. Our lessons about erosion and the processes that shape Earth come back into play here as we talk about islands, peninsulas, lakes, rivers, and more. Using prior experiences and background knowledge, our students share the places they've vacationed and how they traveled there, so they all learn from each other. To ensure equity, we make it very clear that a vacation doesn't mean you've flown somewhere or even traveled a great distance. We teach our students that a vacation can be any time you take a break from your normal routine. Go to grandma's house over the weekend? That's a vacation! We want every student to feel included in the discussion no matter their traveling experience.

As we share these destinations, each student writes their name on a sticky note and we post it on our large pull-down map at the front of the room. We then add a little math practice connection and sort the places we've traveled in various ways: tropical locations, colder climates, near or far, and so on. This leads us to point out a location on the map far out in the middle of the Pacific Ocean. Then we spring the news that we'll be taking a class trip to Hawaii! Screams of excitement are inevitably followed by at least one student saying, "My brother told me we don't really go to Hawaii." Our response is always the same: "The more you use your imagination over the next week, the more fun you're going to have!"

To make the unit as believable as possible for even the most hesitant imagination, we ask our students to tap into the knowledge they learned during our unit on weather and weather patterns. We get out our globe and discuss weather and temperature as we move closer to the equator. We use everything we've learned about warm places to brainstorm a list of things our students need to pack in their suitcase for our trip to Hawaii. Cue the Kevin McCallister line from *Home Alone*: "Pack my suitcase?" Yep, pack your suitcase, kids—we're going to Hawaii!

So how are we getting there? Once again using the globe, we talk about all the ways humans can travel around Earth. First, we discuss how we travel to and from school each day. Is that a way we'd get to Hawaii? Then we talk about the train systems that run around our communities and into bigger cities. Could we take a train to get to Hawaii? No? So how do we travel a great distance over land and sea? An airplane! Yes! We're taking off on Kindergarten Airlines!

Our travel begins on a Friday when our students bring those packed suitcases to school and check in to get their flight ticket.

We take some time to fill out luggage tags and hand out boarding passes before we board our mock flight. The excitement will be uncontainable as kids discuss what it's like to fly in an airplane: "I can't believe we're flying today!" That's the reaction we hope for! We're lucky enough to have a narrow space on a stage in our building that makes a perfect airplane, but a simple rearrangement of chairs in the classroom or in a hallway would work just as well.

We serve snacks and juice while watching a short movie. Then it's time for our layover, which just happens to be a weekend long. How do we convince students we're on a layover and still on vacation? While they're on the flight, one teacher hides all the luggage in a closet or another area out of sight. When we land at our layover destination, kids immediately notice the missing luggage. We then explain that we've stopped for the weekend but that when we arrive at our final destination on Monday, our luggage will be off the plane and waiting for us.

During our math block, we cap the day off with a paper airplane contest. Each student makes their own airplane and takes a turn throwing it and measuring the distance it travels. This turns into a review as well as number recognition, measurement, and greater than/less than knowledge as students work together to compare the distances their planes flew.

As students head home for their weekend layover, full of excitement from flight day, they have no idea what's in store when they return on Monday. But after a week full of reading and learning about landforms, oceans, travel, and Hawaii, they have an idea of what it's like to write packing lists and vacation plans. They take home their paper airplanes plus new knowledge of how to measure, compare, and contrast distance. Best of all, they leave engaged and more excited than ever to come back to school on Monday!

ALOHA! WE HAVE ARRIVED!

On Monday, we arrive in Hawaii and explore a different theme each day of the week. These themed days can be done in any order you choose, but here's how we did it:

- Arrival Day: learn about leis, the islands, and Hawaiian culture.
- Volcano Day: learn about volcanoes and do a fun experiment.
- Ocean Day: learn about the animals and plants that live in the ocean around Hawaii.
- Beach Party Day: celebrate the beach with a beach party bash!
- Luau Day: say aloha with a Hawaiian feast and party!

THE SCIENCE BOX

VOLCANO DAY

LEARNING FOCUS

In this volcano experiment, students will visually experience an acid-based reaction resulting in the production of massive quantities of carbon dioxide bubbling out of the top of their homemade volcanoes. This mimics the effects of an actual volcano. Once you've collected the listed supplies, you'll be ready to go.

WHAT'S IN THE BOX?

- Dr. Science letter
- Sand
- Plastic tub
- Cylinder container
- Baking soda

- Vinegar
- Food coloring
- Directions/experiment card
- Recording sheets

In the previous week's discussion of landforms, students learned that Hawaii's land masses were formed by volcanic activity. This topic sparks so much wonder and amazement that we're sure to get some great questions. The mere mention of the word *volcano* is enough to excite young learners and instantly engage them. Trust us—Kim has thirteen years of volcano experiments under her belt, and her students are always hooked. When Volcano Day rolls around, we transform part of our classroom into a volcano to enhance the learning experience. Brown dollar-store tablecloths, a hula hoop, red streamers, and some fishing line can go a long way to create a brand-new, volcano-themed learning space in the classroom. What better way to learn *about* volcanoes than *in* a volcano?

The smiles say it all. We learn how volcanoes are formed, the parts of volcanoes, differences between active and dormant volcanoes, and . . . drumroll, please . . . we make a volcano of our very own!

Using a tub of wet sand, each student takes a turn pushing up sand until they've formed a mountain, simulating how volcanoes form over time. This is a perfect opportunity to review the parts of a volcano. Focus on the top, which students now know is called the *crater*. Push the cylinder container into the center of the mountain so that it resembles a crater. This is what will house the next part of your experiment. No volcano demonstration is complete without an explosion of some type, so finish off Volcano Day with just that. A simple mixture of baking soda and red-dyed vinegar does the trick. Your volcano will explode, and the eruption will be mirrored by the excitement inside your volcano-flipped classroom!

Volcanoes

1 Bury a cup in the sand.

2 Add baking soda.

3 Add vinegar.

4 What happened?

THE SCIENCE BOX

OCEAN DAY

LEARNING FOCUS

The focus of this lesson is identifying animal and plant life. There is also some cross-curricular content tied in because students will count the animals. While swimming through the ocean (hallway, multipurpose room, etc.) students will count the various animal and plant species they see and record the number in their ocean counting books. They can also use prior knowledge of ocean life to label the pictures in their books.

WHAT'S IN THE BOX?

- Dr. Science letter
- Ocean counting books
- Markers
- Animal fact sheets
- Directions/experiment card

Throughout the week, we read stories and nonfiction texts about the wildlife and plants found in Hawaii and the surrounding ocean. We use this information to make connections with the animals and plants our students are more familiar with. Our previous studies come back into play as we compare and contrast animals that live where we do with those in Hawaii. Do animals in Hawaii have to adapt to their environment differently than animals here? Our young scientists become marine biologists during this unit as we take a dive in our mock ocean to learn about various sea life.

Of course, you flew over the ocean on your flight to Hawaii. Ask for parent volunteers to help magically transform your classroom into an underwater experience for your learners. Giant construction paper creatures and plants (previously introduced in the unit) cover the walls and ceiling of the stage to create an immersive environment. Jellyfish hang from the ceiling, starfish are taped to the floor, and kelp is taped to the walls to simulate growing seaweeds. These are just a few examples of what kids will come across on their dive.

Students will see familiar species, but we also want to strategically introduce them to animals and plants they might never have heard of before as they "swim" in the ocean and work with their dive teams to identify and count the ocean creatures.

BEACH PARTY DAY

LEARNING FOCUS

By applying sunscreen to paper, students will see how ultraviolet waves can be blocked, preventing the paper from fading. This experience will demonstrate that while the sun provides many things, it can also be dangerous, so we need to protect our body and belongings. Be sure to check with students' parents before applying sunscreen to children's hands. Some children may be sensitive to sunscreen ingredients.

WHAT'S IN THE BOX?

- Dr. Science letter
- Sunscreen
- Directions/experiment card
- Recording sheets
- Construction paper (make sure it can fade; do not use fadeless paper)

No Hawaiian vacation would be complete without a trip to the beach, right? This day is a perfect time to review your scientific study of light and shadows as well as the pirate activity (as students lather on sunscreen). We teach a very important lesson with this experiment.

Use the sunscreen Dr. Science delivers to paint one hand of each student. Then have them stamp their handprint on a piece of construction paper. Leave this outside during the remainder of your beach party and let the sunscreen do its job. Students are always amazed to see that the paper faded around their handprints but not where the sunscreen covered the paper. This is an awesome visual that reiterates the importance of sunscreen.

Beach Party Day finds students soaking up the sun while learning and doing beach activities like volleyball, surfing, seashell collecting, and more. Keep up the cross-curricular connection and tie into social studies by learning about Hawaiian culture and history. You can read and watch videos about how hula dancers tell stories through the dances. You can also compare and contrast the culture and way of life in Hawaii to students' own experiences. How is life on the islands of Hawaii similar and different to your students' lives? Or, if you're a teacher in Hawaii, how is life different in other places? Math

ties in as young scientists discover, describe, and sort seashells on a sand table. They discuss characteristics of the shells and sort by size, shape, and color while sharing stories of their own experiences with finding seashells or other items outdoors.

LUAU DAY

The week of Hawaiian study closes with a full-blown kindergarten (or your grade level) luau! Limbo contests spark discussions about balance, and pineapple bowling focuses conversation on speed, forces, and interactions, recalling your previous ramp-building activity. Dancing, food, and fun are the perfect components of a successful luau, and we recommend using all three to celebrate everything your students have learned.

One of our favorite parts of this experience is how reluctant the kids are to "go home" at the end of the week. Whether or not they've experienced a real tropical vacation before, they leave this week feeling like they did. And while they don't take home their own Science Box, they do get to take home a paper suitcase chock full of recording sheets, crafts, and more. It's an opportunity for a child to enjoy something they might not get to experience outside of school. Most importantly, the connections they make throughout the week will not only enhance the learning experience; they will help create memories that last long after the week is over.

Of course, certain specifics of these lessons might not apply for educators living in Hawaii or for students who are from Hawaii/of Hawaiian descent. We hope teachers in Hawaii can adapt this idea to other locations.

13

THE FINAL CHALLENGE

Now what? That's a question we get from teachers all the time. Our answer is always the same: start small. Teaching isn't easy—let's get that straight. Nothing about your job is, has been, or ever will be considered easy. We totally understand that we just threw an abundance of explorations, experiments, and ideas your way, and we know implementing new things can be tough. We designed and integrated these activities over the course of years in our own classrooms. We didn't start them all at once. However, the simplicity of the experiments and explorations we created combined with the ease of implementing them through weekly Science Box introductions makes it so much easier. Our goal was to make it as simple as possible to craft learning experiences that are engaging and exciting for our students. We hope you've found some ideas in this book that have inspired you to do the same in your own classroom.

So really, now what? Where do you begin your own journey through the NGSS and these experiments? Do you draw lines on some T-shirts with a Sharpie to create lab coats? Do you attach ribbon, hem tape, and buttons? Do you grab an extra cardboard box and draw some science symbols on the side? Do you decorate a plastic storage tub with science stickers and flair? Guess what: it doesn't matter! Let's repeat that. It. Does. Not. Matter! We each approached our Science Box journeys differently, and you might approach yours differently from the teacher next door to you. The beauty of it is that no matter how you implement these ideas, your kids won't know the difference. Adam's students love their Sharpie lab coats just as much as Kim's students love their tape-and-buttons ones. We wouldn't attribute any of our success to the way our supplies look. Sure, let's be honest—the lab coats and goggles help. But the experiences far exceed the materials. The real credit goes to the novelty of the Science Box concept. Our students love it all because it's something different, they're excited to open the box each week, and every single exploration or experiment engages them in new ways.

The one thing we want to remind you to do is keep the process front and center. While the subject matter is important, what we're most concerned with is following the scientific method or the STEM steps. This framework provides the structure for learning now and in the future. Take some time to make charts, sticky notes, or index cards to help you remember these steps until you become comfortable with them. This will free up your brain to spend its time learning the new material you're presenting.

You'll see your students begin to use the process during playtime while solving problems in the block center, maker space, and other such areas. This is when you know it has been internalized. Go ahead and pat yourself on the back! You may want to look at the science experiments and STEM activities that you already do. Are you using the process to enhance understanding of the topic at hand? What tweaks can you easily make so that you follow the process? Could you add a recording sheet to ensure you're following the steps alongside your students? Could you make an experiment card to be sure the children are learning how to follow directions? Do you have another trick up your sleeve to help you teach this valuable process? We bet you do!

As we said earlier in this book, the real goal of all learning is to build schema—a foundation on which future learning can be built. By going through the STEM steps and conducting science experiments, children are building an understanding of how scientists, engineers, and mathematicians solve problems. This approach to teaching and learning will extend well beyond your own classroom. Your students will carry the processes that you put in place to other classrooms and into their daily lives.

Science lends itself to cross-curricular connections. It's a great way to encourage the reluctant reader to find purpose and pleasure in reading, for example. Meanwhile, they'll be learning how to predict and infer, how to identify real-world problems, how to develop the comprehension strategies we so desperately want them to have. This is possible because supplying high-interest nonfiction texts and providing extension activities will enhance your students' reading excitement. Children will remember the books because of the associated activities, experiments, and experiences. This is so much better than reading them once and returning them to the shelf. Kids will remember the books that *we* love—the ones that we want to spend extra time with.

Science also extends into many of the math standards. Graphing children's hypotheses will give you an instant math lesson in comparing numbers and how to organize that data into graphs. Measurement and counting can be included throughout the graphing and observing phases of an experiment. Science is a vehicle to demonstrate the importance of math and how we use it in our daily lives.

While these are all great reasons to love science, when it comes down to it, we love science because it's just so fun and engaging. Reluctant learners will sit up and take note when it's time for science. They don't feel lost. Remember, science can level the learning playing field. Many children are good with their hands, and while a work sheet or reading assessment might not reveal their strength, a design process might let them demonstrate their understanding of a lesson. The hands-on component of science provides an opportunity for concrete understanding of complicated topics. The beauty of it all is that children make it seem far less complicated. Students who don't excel in math or reading can find success and even shine in science.

Are you ready to get started? Just take a chance. Plan one activity. See how your kids light up. This will give you all the feels, we promise! Whether you're a Sharpie-and-simplify teacher like Adam or a ribbons-and-buttons teacher like Kim, your kids won't care. They'll be excited because you're excited. They'll be eager to learn because you're eager to teach. Most importantly, they will be exploring, experimenting, and experiencing learning like never before.

Knock, knock. Dr. Science is at your door delivering exploration and experimental fun! Are you ready to answer?

ACKNOWLEDGMENTS

We both owe a huge thanks to all the wonderful educators who contributed to this book: Katie Blue Mense, Dr. Lori Elliott, Mary Amoson, Shannon Cunningham-Lanning, LeAnna Wolkis Goldstein, Hilary Statum, and Kim Jordano. Your contributions helped make this book the best it could be.

Thank you to the many associations, professional organizations, companies, and school districts that have placed their trust in us. Thank you to Ryan, Bill, and everyone involved with ILASCD for your continued support of the two of us—the place we first met and presented together!

To all of our fellow presenters, we are thankful for your friendship, encouragement, and support. And to every teacher whom we have ever taught with, we appreciate both the professional and personal growth that came from our experiences.

Thank you to the parents and families who trusted us with your children throughout our years in the classroom. Watching your children learn has been our greatest teacher. It is through them that we honed our craft as educators!

To the millions of other educators who are working nonstop to make school the best place it possibly can be, thank you for all you do! Thank you for opening your classroom doors and inviting us in to observe, participate, and model! You are our driving force.

Last, but not least, thank you to Dave, Tara, Wendy, and everyone at Dave Burgess Consulting for your support of this project and the two of us. We are blessed to be part of the DBC family of authors.

ADAM

I want to start by thanking my biggest supporters, my family. Trisha, Olivia, and Landon are my reason for doing all that I do. Trisha, thank you for believing in me and giving me all of your support of any project I take on. Olivia and Landon, thank you for being my biggest fans! I love the three of you more than you'll ever know.

Thank you to my mom and dad, my mother-in-law, Gloria, Jodie, Shannon, Lily, Dean, Maurey, Michael, Jon, Jen, Scott, Nanny Lois, and Grandma Caroll. Family is everything to me, and none of my success would be possible without you all.

KIM

Beyond thankful to my partner in life and amazing tech support system, Andy! Thank you for helping me with all the tech issues and encouraging me to continue to share my passion for teaching our youngest learners. I'm incredibly appreciative of Megan and Ginny and their willingness to be guinea pigs in our shared desire to provide engaging experiences through their classrooms. To all four of my grown-up kids, Megan, Nick, Tyler, and Ginny, I love you guys. I am so proud of you as you raise kiddos who always ask the why, want to be good stewards of our earth, and are kind people. I'm grateful for my most important job, being Gammy to these four amazing grandchildren—Matthew, Brody, Sonny, and Charlotte. Most importantly, I'm thankful that God gave me the passion and the desire to teach the littlest learners!

ABOUT THE AUTHORS

KIM ADSIT

Kim Adsit is a master teacher and a national speaker. With thirty years of teaching experience, Kim shares her love and enthusiasm for teaching our youngest learners through play and meaningful interactions across the content areas. Her mutual love and respect of teachers is evident by her highly sought after high-energy presentations. If Kim is not presenting or coaching, she can be found in the classrooms of her daughter or daughter-in-law lending a helping hand, leading a lesson, or just hanging out with the kids! Andy, her husband of nearly forty years, is her right-hand man with all tech issues! They have two amazing children, Megan, who is married to Nick, and Tyler, who is married to Ginny. Kim's greatest joy is her four grandchildren: Matthew, Brody, Sonny, and Charlotte.

For more information on where to see Kim speak, or to book her for your own school, visit her blog **kindergals.blogspot.com**.

 kindergals   kindergals

ADAM PETERSON

Adam Peterson is an award-winning educator from Illinois and a nationally recognized speaker. After spending more than a decade as a kindergarten teacher, Adam now uses his knowledge and talents to inspire, educate, and motivate other teachers to create classrooms that encourage creativity, play, and hands-on learning. Adam is a TEDx speaker, and his message of making the world a brighter place through his Be the Yellow talk and campaign have reached schools around the globe with videos and assemblies for kids. Being a believer that family comes first, Adam spends every free second he has with his beautiful wife, Trisha, their two amazing children, and their dog, Auggie.

For more information on where to see Adam speak or to book him for your own school, visit his website **adampetersoneducation.com**.

adampetersoneducation   **Adam Peterson Education**
adampetersoneducation.com
makesomeonesdayyellow.com

MORE FROM

DAVE BURGESS Consulting, Inc.

Since 2012, DBCI has published books that inspire and equip
educators to be their best. For more information on our titles
or to purchase bulk orders for your school, district, or book
study, visit DaveBurgessConsulting.com/DBCIbooks.

LIKE A PIRATE™ SERIES

Teach Like a PIRATE by Dave Burgess
eXPlore Like a PIRATE by Michael Matera
Learn Like a PIRATE by Paul Solarz
Plan Like a PIRATE by Dawn M. Harris
Play Like a PIRATE by Quinn Rollins
Run Like a PIRATE by Adam Welcome
Tech Like a PIRATE by Matt Miller

LEAD LIKE A PIRATE™ SERIES

Lead Like a PIRATE by Shelley Burgess and Beth Houf
Balance Like a PIRATE by Jessica Cabeen, Jessica Johnson, and
    Sarah Johnson
Lead beyond Your Title by Nili Bartley
Lead with Appreciation by Amber Teamann and Melinda Miller
Lead with Culture by Jay Billy
Lead with Instructional Rounds by Vicki Wilson
Lead with Literacy by Mandy Ellis
She Leads by Dr. Rachael George and Majalise W. Tolan

LEADERSHIP & SCHOOL CULTURE

Beyond the Surface of Restorative Practices by Marisol Rerucha
Change the Narrative by Henry J. Turner and Kathy Lopes
Choosing to See by Pamela Seda and Kyndall Brown
Culturize by Jimmy Casas
Discipline Win by Andy Jacks
Escaping the School Leader's Dunk Tank by Rebecca Coda and
    Rick Jetter
Fight Song by Kim Bearden
From Teacher to Leader by Starr Sackstein
If the Dance Floor Is Empty, Change the Song by Joe Clark
The Innovator's Mindset by George Couros
It's OK to Say "They" by Christy Whittlesey
Kids Deserve It! by Todd Nesloney and Adam Welcome
Leading the Whole Teacher by Allyson Apsey
Let Them Speak by Rebecca Coda and Rick Jetter
The Limitless School by Abe Hege and Adam Dovico
Live Your Excellence by Jimmy Casas
Next-Level Teaching by Jonathan Alsheimer
The Pepper Effect by Sean Gaillard
Principaled by Kate Barker, Kourtney Ferrua, and Rachael George
The Principled Principal by Jeffrey Zoul and Anthony McConnell
Relentless by Hamish Brewer
The Secret Solution by Todd Whitaker, Sam Miller, and Ryan Donlan
Start. Right. Now. by Todd Whitaker, Jeffrey Zoul, and Jimmy Casas
Stop. Right. Now. by Jimmy Casas and Jeffrey Zoul
Teachers Deserve It by Rae Hughart and Adam Welcome
Teach Your Class Off by CJ Reynolds
They Call Me "Mr. De" by Frank DeAngelis
Thrive through the Five by Jill M. Siler
Unmapped Potential by Julie Hasson and Missy Lennard
When Kids Lead by Todd Nesloney and Adam Dovico
Word Shift by Joy Kirr
Your School Rocks by Ryan McLane and Eric Lowe

TECHNOLOGY & TOOLS

50 Things to Go Further with Google Classroom by Alice Keeler and Libbi Miller

50 Things You Can Do with Google Classroom by Alice Keeler and Libbi Miller

140 Twitter Tips for Educators by Brad Currie, Billy Krakower, and Scott Rocco

Block Breaker by Brian Aspinall

Building Blocks for Tiny Techies by Jamila "Mia" Leonard

Code Breaker by Brian Aspinall

The Complete EdTech Coach by Katherine Goyette and Adam Juarez

Control Alt Achieve by Eric Curts

The Esports Education Playbook by Chris Aviles, Steve Isaacs, Christine Lion-Bailey, and Jesse Lubinsky

Google Apps for Littles by Christine Pinto and Alice Keeler

Master the Media by Julie Smith

Raising Digital Leaders by Jennifer Casa-Todd

Reality Bytes by Christine Lion-Bailey, Jesse Lubinsky, and Micah Shippee, PhD

Sail the 7 Cs with Microsoft Education by Becky Keene and Kathi Kersznowski

Shake Up Learning by Kasey Bell

Social LEADia by Jennifer Casa-Todd

Stepping Up to Google Classroom by Alice Keeler and Kimberly Mattina

Teaching Math with Google Apps by Alice Keeler and Diana Herrington

Teachingland by Amanda Fox and Mary Ellen Weeks

Teaching with Google Jamboard by Alice Keeler and Kimberly Mattina

TEACHING METHODS & MATERIALS

All 4s and 5s by Andrew Sharos

Boredom Busters by Katie Powell

The Classroom Chef by John Stevens and Matt Vaudrey

The Collaborative Classroom by Trevor Muir

Copyrighteous by Diana Gill

CREATE by Bethany J. Petty

Deploying EduProtocols by Kim Voge, with Jon Corippo and Marlena Hebern

Ditch That Homework by Matt Miller and Alice Keeler

Ditch That Textbook by Matt Miller

Don't Ditch That Tech by Matt Miller, Nate Ridgway, and Angelia Ridgway

EDrenaline Rush by John Meehan

Educated by Design by Michael Cohen, The Tech Rabbi

The EduProtocol Field Guide by Marlena Hebern and Jon Corippo

The EduProtocol Field Guide: Book 2 by Marlena Hebern and Jon Corippo

The EduProtocol Field Guide: Math Edition by Lisa Nowakowski and Jeremiah Ruesch

The EduProtocol Field Guide: Social Studies Edition by Dr. Scott M. Petri and Adam Moler

Empowered to Choose: A Practical Guide to Personalized Learning by Andrew Easton

Expedition Science by Becky Schnekser

Frustration Busters by Katie Powell

Fully Engaged by Michael Matera and John Meehan

Game On? Brain On! by Lindsay Portnoy, PhD

Guided Math AMPED by Reagan Tunstall

Innovating Play by Jessica LaBar-Twomy and Christine Pinto

Instructional Coaching Connection by Nathan Lang-Raad

Instant Relevance by Denis Sheeran

Keeping the Wonder by Jenna Copper, Ashley Bible, Abby Gross, and Staci Lamb

LAUNCH by John Spencer and A.J. Juliani

Learning in the Zone by Dr. Sonny Magana

Lights, Cameras, TEACH! by Kevin J. Butler

Make Learning MAGICAL by Tisha Richmond

Pass the Baton by Kathryn Finch and Theresa Hoover

Project-Based Learning Anywhere by Lori Elliott

Pure Genius by Don Wettrick

The Revolution by Darren Ellwein and Derek McCoy

Shift This! by Joy Kirr

Skyrocket Your Teacher Coaching by Michael Cary Sonbert

Spark Learning by Ramsey Musallam

Sparks in the Dark by Travis Crowder and Todd Nesloney

Table Talk Math by John Stevens

Unpack Your Impact by Naomi O'Brien and LaNesha Tabb

The Wild Card by Hope and Wade King

Writefully Empowered by Jacob Chastain

The Writing on the Classroom Wall by Steve Wyborney

You Are Poetry by Mike Johnston

INSPIRATION, PROFESSIONAL GROWTH & PERSONAL DEVELOPMENT

Be REAL by Tara Martin

Be the One for Kids by Ryan Sheehy

The Coach ADVenture by Amy Illingworth

Creatively Productive by Lisa Johnson

Educational Eye Exam by Alicia Ray

The EduNinja Mindset by Jennifer Burdis

Empower Our Girls by Lynmara Colón and Adam Welcome

Finding Lifelines by Andrew Grieve and Andrew Sharos

The Four O'Clock Faculty by Rich Czyz

How Much Water Do We Have? by Pete and Kris Nunweiler

P Is for Pirate by Dave and Shelley Burgess

A Passion for Kindness by Tamara Letter

The Path to Serendipity by Allyson Apsey

Rogue Leader by Rich Czyz

Sanctuaries by Dan Tricarico

Saving Sycamore by Molly B. Hudgens

The SECRET SAUCE by Rich Czyz

Shattering the Perfect Teacher Myth by Aaron Hogan

Stories from Webb by Todd Nesloney

Talk to Me by Kim Bearden

Teach Better by Chad Ostrowski, Tiffany Ott, Rae Hughart, and
    Jeff Gargas

Teach Me, Teacher by Jacob Chastain

Teach, Play, Learn! by Adam Peterson

The Teachers of Oz by Herbie Raad and Nathan Lang-Raad

TeamMakers by Laura Robb and Evan Robb

Through the Lens of Serendipity by Allyson Apsey

The Zen Teacher by Dan Tricarico

Write Here and Now by Dan Tricarico

CHILDREN'S BOOKS

Alpert by LaNesha Tabb

Alpert & Friends by LaNesha Tabb

Beyond Us by Aaron Polansky

Cannonball In by Tara Martin

Dolphins in Trees by Aaron Polansky

I Can Achieve Anything by MoNique Waters

I Want to Be a Lot by Ashley Savage

The Magic of Wonder by Jenna Copper, Ashley Bible, Abby Gross, and Staci Lamb

Micah's Big Question by Naomi O'Brien

The Princes of Serendip by Allyson Apsey

Ride with Emilio by Richard Nares

A Teacher's Top Secret Confidential by LaNesha Tabb

A Teacher's Top Secret: Mission Accomplished by LaNesha Tabb

The Wild Card Kids by Hope and Wade King

Zom-Be a Design Thinker by Amanda Fox

Printed in the USA
CPSIA information can be obtained
at www.ICGtesting.com
LVHW011358031023
760005LV00009B/324